THE CAMEL WITH A JAPI

An Initiative under "Ek Bharat Shreshth Bharat"

AF650318

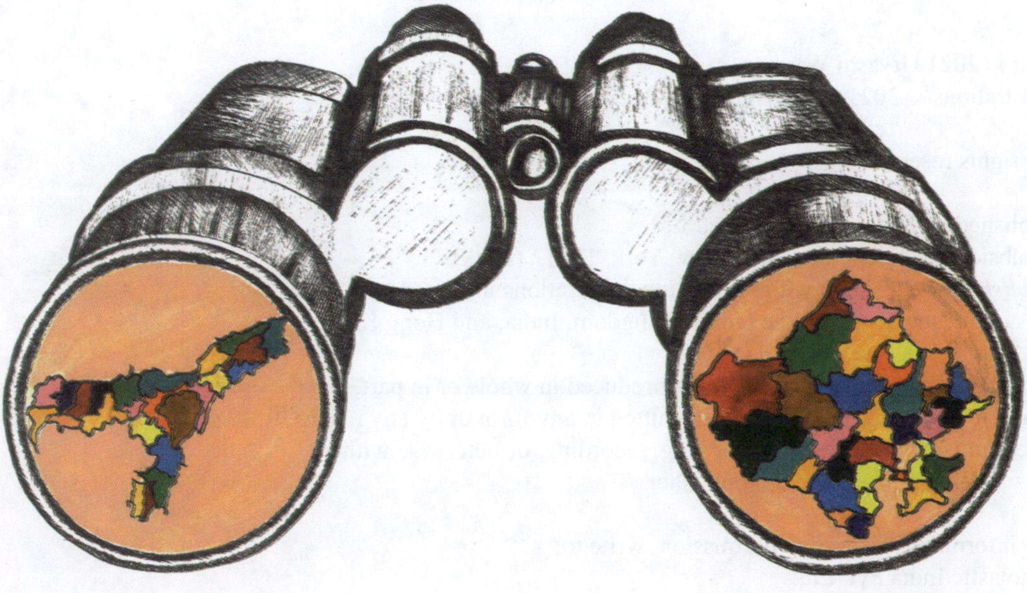

Text © 2021 Urvashi Warman
Illustrations © 2021 Scholastic India Pvt. Ltd.

All rights reserved.

Published by Scholastic India Pvt. Ltd.
A subsidiary of Scholastic Inc., New York, 10012 (USA).
Publishers since 1920, with international operations in Canada, Australia, New Zealand, the United Kingdom, India, and Hong Kong.

No part of this publication may be reproduced in whole or in part, or stored in a retrieval system, or transmitted in any form or by any means, electronic, mechanical, photocopying, recording, or otherwise without the written permission of the publisher.

For information regarding permission, write to:
Scholastic India Pvt. Ltd.
A-27, Ground Floor, Sigma Centre
Infocity-1, Sector 34, Gurgaon-122001 (India)

First edition: December 2021

This reprint edition April 2025

ISBN-13: 978-93-5471-283-8

Printed in India at Acme Print O Pac Pvt. Ltd Noida

The Palace School

THE CAMEL WITH A JAPI

An Illustrated Narrative of Assam and Rajasthan

Urvashi Warman

SCHOLASTIC
New York Toronto London Auckland
Sydney New Delhi Hong Kong

धर्मेन्द्र प्रधान
ଧର୍ମେନ୍ଦ୍ର ପ୍ରଧାନ
Dharmendra Pradhan

सत्यमेव जयते

मंत्री
शिक्षा; कौशल विकास
और उद्यमशीलता
भारत सरकार
Minister
Education; Skill Development
& Entrepreneurship
Government of India

MESSAGE

India is a living embodiment of different cultures which has been breathing for centuries. The way flowers of different shades and fragrances maintain their entity but collectively lend harmony and beauty to a garden, the same way each Indian state has its own distinct culture, which adds to the overall uniqueness of India.

To celebrate this rich cultural diversity, Hon'ble Prime Minister had launched the ***Ek Bharat - Shreshtha Bharat*** programme which has led to a greater mutual understanding and admiration for each other amidst the people. Giving an impetus to this vision, our National Education Policy 2020 also aims at instilling a deep-rooted pride of being Indian amongst students and acquaints them with the rich diversity of India.

I am happy to note that the illustrated novel **'The Camel With A Japi'** has been prepared in the same spirit of enhancing the interaction between the states of Rajasthan and Assam.

I congratulate the students and faculty of The Palace School, Jaipur for undertaking this meaningful initiative that will surely set a quintessential example for other schools to emulate.

(Dharmendra Pradhan)

New Delhi,
Dated 28th July, 2021

सबको शिक्षा, अच्छी शिक्षा

कौशल भारत, कुशल भारत

MOE - Room No. 3, 'C' Wing, 3rd Floor, Shastri Bhavan, New Delhi-110 115, Phone : 91-11-23782387, Fax : 91-11-23382365
MSDE - Room No. 516, 5th Floor, Shram Shakti Bhawan, Rafi Marg, New Delhi-110001, Phone : 91-11-23465810, Fax : 011-23465825
E-mail : minister.sm@gov.in, minister-msde@gov.in

FOREWORD

Ek Bharat Shrestha Bharat, the dream of our visionary Prime Minister Shri Narendra Modi ji, has been aptly enlivened through the book *The Camel with a Japi*, which is an illustrated novel of Assam and Rajasthan.

I feel immense pleasure to note that the students and faculty members of my school have done an interesting research on Rajasthan and Assam for their Art Integrated Learning Projects. It is interesting to note how the information has been collated thereafter into a riveting story of school students who along with their teachers embark upon a journey of discovery about both the States. Having gone through the final draft of the story, I experienced several emotions, chief among them being a sense of deep pride about living in a country of immense diversity. The book discusses at length about the rich culture of Assam and Rajasthan along with their tangible and intangible heritage. It also touches upon topics like economics, trade, biodiversity, climate change, empowerment of women, gender parity among others. It is heartening to note that *The Camel with a Japi* fulfils several tenets of NEP 2020 which stipulate that at all stages of learning one has to adapt storytelling, sports and art integrated education, interdisciplinary and transdisciplinary approach as standard pedagogy. I am happy to note that *The Camel with a Japi* fulfills all these points thereby making it a comprehensive educational document.

I was intrigued to know that the story of the book is mapped as per the Learning Objectives of NCERT. Further, I felt delighted to know that the teachers have gone a step further by deriving case studies from each chapter which cater to various subjects. I am happy that a supplementary book based on these case studies and competency based questions is also under publication.

My sincere compliments to Urvashi Warman for penning down a book which is a tribute to story telling as a powerful pedagogy. I would also like to extend my compliments to the teachers, students and alumni who have been instrumental in putting this beautiful piece of art integrated work together in such an innovative manner.

Maharaja Sawai Man Singh II Museum, Jaipur, takes great pride in bringing forth this wonderful educational document encased in a powerful storyline for all students and teachers of our country.

Jai Hind.

Diya Kumari
Member of Parliament Rajsamand
Rajasthan

ACKNOWLEDGEMENTS

I would like to express my deep and sincere gratitude to Princess Diya Kumari, Founder of The Palace School, for bestowing trust and providing extensive support in this project.

I am deeply honoured to express my sincere gratitude to Ms Anita Karwal, Secretary Education for her guidance and motivation. Her perception of taking learning out of textbooks through graphic novels while fulfilling the learning objectives, gave a fillip to the project of writing a full-length novel. It was Madam Anita Karwal's guidance which made us integrate various art forms across the country along with the narrative.

I would also like to extend my deep gratitude to Shri Manoj Ahuja, Chairman CBSE, for his motivating presence and guidance. I am humbled by the time accorded by him to go through the draft of the book and provide valuable inputs.

My special thanks to Madam Rama Datt, Executive Trustee, MSMSII Museum, Jaipur, for her all time, encouragement and motivation.

I am falling short of words of gratitude to thank Dr Rima Hooja, Director, MSMSII Museum, Jaipur, for patiently going through all the historical and cultural aspects covered in the book. Being a renowned historian, her insights were extremely valuable. I am also grateful to Dr. Jyotsna Devi, Retired Professor Assam Agricultural University Jorhat, Assam, for giving her most valuable suggestions on the content connected to Assam.

I acknowledge with gratitude my debt of thanks to Maharaj Karan Vijay Singh of Jodhpur and Thakur Lokendra Rathore for their valuable inputs and support.

I am grateful to Ms Asha Mishra, Educator and Academic Consultant, along with Ms Chandrika Das, Research Scholar, The English and Foreign Languages University, Hyderabad for sparing their invaluable time for amending the text.

I would like to thank the teachers of SV Public School, Scindia Kanya Vidyalaya, Gwalior, Sri Sathya Sai School, Indore, Shanti Asiatic School, Jaipur, Springdales School, Pusa Road, Delhi, Sanskar School, Jaipur and The Palace School, Jaipur, for taking out time from their busy schedule to help curate the book.

I cannot really express enough thanks to appreciate the teachers of The Palace School who helped me with the research work and drafted a few chapters for the book—Dr Sumedha Tiwari, Ms Puja Garg, Ms Bhavna Godha, Ms Shamim Khan, Ms Neha Goyal, Ms Vandana Sharma, Ms Priyanka Mathur, Mr Praneet Shivhare, Ms Preet Shandilya, Ms Seema Gupta, Mr Sanjay Vaid, Ms Kaishena Joshi, Ms Neha Chaturvedi, Ms Monica Khatak, Ms Preity Bhatnagar, Ms Shalini Goswami and Ms Sangeeta Singh Bhati.

I feel happy to state that editing was also done by a few students of our school—Saif Ur Rehman of Grade Six (2020-21), Aadya Sharma of Grade X (2020-21) and Amishi Garg of Grade X (2020-21). By the time the book goes into print, they would have gone up to a higher grade. I wish to convey my humble thanks to these young editors.

Excellent information was also shared by our alumnus Siddharth Kothari, who is currently studying Textile Design in NIFT, Bengaluru. Siddharth also spared his time to edit the book and assisted Mr Raju Kumawat for clicking photographs too.

My completion of this project could not have been accomplished without the support and creative inputs of the IT Team—Ms Puja Garg, Ms Neelima Baj, Ms Sangeeta Sharma, Ms Anisha Rajawat, Miss Priyanka Gupta and Ms Uma Saini.

No words of appreciation can do justice to the breathtaking illustrations done by the art team—Ms Rekha Karnawat, Ms Meeta Mathur, Ms Vandana Yadav, and Mr Raju Kumawat who also clicked some superb photographs for the book. Thank you! Additionally, I would like to thank my wonderful alumni for the superb sketches made by them—Sakshi Aggarwal, Ani Agarwal, Khushi Sharma, Yadunandan Singh Bhati. Proud of you!

A word of appreciation is extended for Shri Mohan Saini and Shri Mukesh Sharma who worked tirelessly to integrate the text with the illustrations.

I would like to specially thank and acknowledge the contributions of Ms Poonam Sharma from The Palace School, who has been a pillar of strength during the entire process of bringing out the book. This book would have never seen the light of day had it not been for her sincere and dedicated efforts. Thank you for making it possible.

Finally, I also take this opportunity to thank my caring, loving and supportive family—my better half, Anil Warman and my son, Ajay Singh for being very patient as I burnt the midnight oil while writing the book and for giving me the time and space to work without distractions. Your encouragement during difficult moments is beyond appreciation.

Last but not least, my heartfelt gratitude to Shri Sandeep Sethi, Director Education MSMSII Museum, Jaipur, for his constant support and guidance at every stage of work. The book would not have become a comprehensive educational document without his critical and valuable inputs. Shri Sandeep Sethi has been the wind beneath my wings. Thank you, sir! A final word of gratitude to the readers who have picked up this book to read... I hope you enjoy reading it as much as I have enjoyed writing it.

Urvashi Warman

PICTURE CREDITS

We are grateful to Maharaja Sawai Man Singh II Museum, Jaipur, for allowing us to access rare photographs of—Govind Dev ji, Shri Shila Mata Temple, The Old World Charm, Vintage Jaipur, Reminiscing the Hawa Mahal, H. H. Maharaja Sawai Padmanabh Singh & Winners of The Polo World Cup.

We thank Princess Diya Kumari Foundation (PDKF) for sharing pictures of Princess Diya Kumari with PDKF Ladies.

We are also grateful to The Media Office, The City Palace, Udaipur ©MMCF for enriching the narrative by sharing beautiful pictures of Ekling ji and The City Palace, Udaipur.

We thank Shri Ramu Ramdev for sharing his painting of Bani Thani, Ms Puja Garg for the photograph of Make Shift Shelters and Ms Hina Nahta for the photographs of the Circuit house and the Dumb waiter.

We acknowledge the use of pictures from the web. The links are given below:

Gadhganesh
(https://commons.wikimedia.org/wiki/File:Jaipur_03-016_38_Garh_Ganesh_Temple.jpg)

Citra Bhagavata
(http://upload.wikimedia.org/wikipedia/commons/thumb/1/15/Citra_Bhagavata_illustration_1.jpg/394px- Citra_Bhagavata_illustration_1.jpg)

Folio From a Culpsutra Manuscript
(https://images.metmuseum.org/CRDImages/as/original/DT6940.jpg Golden Oriole (https://upload.wikimedia.org/wikipedia/commons/thumb/6/67/Golden_Oriole_from_Dresser%27s_Birds_of_Europe.jpg/596px- Golden_Oriole_from_Dresser%27s_Birds_of_Europe.jpg)

Hollong tree
https://upload.wikimedia.org/wikipedia/commons/thumb/1/19/Sapling_of_Hollong_tree_%28Dipterocarpus_macrocarpus%29%2C_the_state_tree_of_Assam.jpg/220px- Sapling_of_Hollong_tree_%28Dipterocarpus_macrocarpus%29%2C_the_state_tree_of_Assam.jpg)

Gaur Bos
(https://upload.wikimedia.org/wikipedia/commons/thumb/0/05/Gaur-Bos_gaurus.jpg/800px-Gaur-Bos_gaurus.jpg)

State Tree
(https://upload.wikimedia.org/wikipedia/commons/6/6d/Khejri.jpg)

Making of pots
(http://majulilandscape.gov.in/thumbs/05.jpg)

Rainwater harvesting
(https://upload.wikimedia.org/wikipedia/commons/thumb/d/db/Rainwater_harvesting_tank%2C_India.jpg/300px- Rainwater_harvesting_tank%2C_India.jpg)

Sonar Quila
(https://upload.wikimedia.org/wikipedia/commons/thumb/4/47/Jaisalmer_forteresse.jpg/1280px-Jaisalmer_forteresse.jpg)

Camellia sinesis
(https://upload.wikimedia.org/wikipedia/commons/thumb/7/71/Csinensis.jpg/220px-Csinensis.jpg)

Chittorgarh Fort
(https://upload.wikimedia.org/wikipedia/commons/thumb/3/3a/Chittorgarh_fort.JPG/300px-Chittorgarh_fort.JPG)

Bhavai
(https://i1.wp.com/www.auchitya.com/wp-content/uploads/2021/01/bhavai-dance.jpg?fit=1024%2C680&ssl=1)

Kalbelia
(https://commons.wikimedia.org/wiki/File:Kalbeliadance.jpg)

Molela
(https://i.pinimg.com/564x/ 29/99/27/2999271e7643ef9ad005f0fcd63fbc8e.jpg wikimedia.org)

Rajasthani turban
(https://it.wikivoyage.org/wiki/File:Rajasthan2105b.jpg)

Satra theatre
(https://commons.wikimedia.org/wiki/File:MUKHA_SILPA,_Majuli,_Assam.jpg)

CONTENTS

RAJASTHAN

PREFACE

The *Camel with a Japi* was conceived with the idea of collating the art integrated projects done by the students of The Palace School as part of their subject enrichment activities outlined by CBSE. It is a work of love, dedicated to our Prime Minister Shri Narendra Modi ji's vision of 'Ek Bharat Shreshth Bharat'.

The information provided by the students and later by the teachers too,has been weaved into a riveting tale of five students who along with their teachers take two educators from France on a whirlwind tour of Rajasthan, briefing them about Assam simultaneously.

The most enriching part about writing this book has been the deep research which has gone into it. Selecting the information to portray and how to do it in an interesting manner was not an easy task. It was also challenging to map the story as per the learning objectives outlined by NCERT, as mapping the narrative would make the book a proper educational document. This exercise made us realize that it was not difficult to have an integrated approach to teaching learning process. Thus, it proved to be an extremely enriching experience for the teachers.

As the chapters took shape, the art department swung into action. They prepared illustrations using various art forms from all across the country and beyond. Different mediums like water colours, oil, acrylic, pencil sketches and photographs have been used to enliven the narrative.

The book is an excellent guide to art lovers who would find fine examples of the rich art heritage of our country.

Curation of the novel was an exhaustive affair. Thanks to the guidance of Shri Sandeep Sethi ji, Director Education MSMSII Museum, we were able to send the novel to several schools to get their valuable inputs. Curation was also done by our school students as well as the alumni. It was heartening to get a positive response from the student body.

The Camel with a Japi is an honest effort to make our students appreciate and respect the immense diversity in our country.

We would be very happy to get your feedback. Please share your review on thecamelwithajapi@gmail.com

Happy Reading!

Urvashi Warman
Principal
The Palace School

ART FORMS USED FOR ILLUSTRATIONS

1) Warli art
2) Bengali alpana
3) Miniature painting
4) Cross hatching
5) Line drawing
6) Block printing
7) Bittu art
8) Mandala art
9) Zentagle Art
10) Udisa pattachitra (coffee painting)
11) Madhubani painting
12) Kalamkari painting
13) Gond painting
14) Phad painting
15) Doodle art
16) Tenga art from Tanzania
17) Pencil Sketches

PRELUDE

Hello! My name is Debina, and I will be taking you down my memory lane to one of the best times I have had during my school life.

Let me now introduce myself.

The Palace School

My name is Debina Barua. My parents hail from Assam. Although I was born in Guwahati, Assam, I have grown up in Jaipur, the capital of Rajasthan. I study in The Palace School, which was founded by Princess Diya Kumari of Jaipur. Honestly speaking, I am very proud of my school! It is situated inside the magnificent City Palace, which is not only the home of Princess Diya Kumari and her family but is also a very famous museum.

It was last year that our English teacher, Mrs Kalpana Rai told us about the visit of two French teachers to our school. Apparently, they were coming to check whether they would find it feasible to partner with our school. They had to choose one school from Rajasthan and another from Assam for a Student and Teacher Exchange Programme.

We were all told to be on our best behaviour and to contain our mischievous ways till their visit.

I was pleasantly surprised when Kalpana ma'am selected me to be a part of the escort team. I was told that the reason I was selected was that the French teachers had requested to bring on board somebody who could simultaneously brief them about Assam. So, who would be a better candidate than me! I was super excited and was sure that I was heading for some of the best days of my school life.

Here begins the virtual journey of all that happened during those days. I will be your narrator as we start the narration from the first day of the arrival of the French team.

But before we start, let me introduce you to our Indian team. Our team consisted of two teachers and five students.

Amongst the teachers, we had Mrs Kalpana Rai, our English teacher. Mrs Rai is a tall, elegant lady whom we all look up with awe due to her immense knowledge and magnetic personality. Most of us wished fervently to emulate her style and grace upon growing up.

Then we had Shri Bhuvan Misra, our Sanskrit teacher.

Misra sir is an adorable person with a fine sense of humour and extremely innovative ways of teaching.Those of us, who had the good fortune of studying Sanskrit from him, swore by the subject and many of us plan to take up Sanskrit for higher studies so we can delve into research of mathematical and scientific concepts propounded by our ancient Indian texts.

Amongst the students, let me introduce you first to Gauransh. Gauransh is a fact geek, (excuse me for saying so!)

He is a walking encyclopaedia of knowledge of just about everything under the sun. He can rattle off facts and figures as though reciting from the book or computer, without batting an eyelid. We were surprised when he was chosen to be a part of our team, as he is completely missing out on his interpersonal skills.

"And that's one of the reasons for choosing him, apart from his knowledge factor," said Ms Kalpana Rai emphatically, when I expressed my doubts about his inability to mingle with people easily.

So, there he was, Gauransh, along with his two constant companions, his tab and his pimples (sorry for being so cheeky!).

Then there is Priyamvada and Meera, my best friends. Priyamvada, Meera and I are together called 'The Three Musketeers', and don't we love that!

Meera is the loquacious one amongst us all. Her cheerful, bubbly nature is absolutely lovable.

Priyamvada, on the other hand, is quieter, comparatively, but she has a great sense of humour and her quiet demeanour can be quite misleading at times as she is equally capable of doing mischievous things as Meera and I.

We could feel the envy of all our classmates for being together on this unique trip.

Last but not least is Rajeev Pandey, The Rogue (that's what we call him!). Rajeev is a complete package of intelligence, wit, humour, mischief, well, the list is endless, but he actually

defines what it means to be an all-rounder… good in sports, academics, co-curricular activities… you name it, and he excels in it. He was, you could say, the perfect choice for the trip.

So, here we are, eagerly awaiting the arrival of the two French teachers.

It is November 14, 2019 and we are at the main gate of our school, waiting to accord a traditional welcome to our guests.

Chapter 1

THE WELCOME

We awaited the arrival of the two French teachers with bated breath. I had helped Meera to make the *Rangoli* at the entrance while Rajeev along with Priyamvada stood with a garland each to welcome the guests. Our Principal, Dr Sadhna Singh, stood with us, surveying all arrangements with a critical eye. Gauransh hovered around the *Maandna* (floor design), taking rapid measurements which mystified us. He refused to tell us what he was thinking, even after being asked repeatedly. We gave up. Little did we realise how this genius' mind worked!

At last, our teachers drove in with the two guests. We were introduced formally. We looked at them curiously, so much so that Meera had to nudge us to quit staring!

Mr Jean Pierre and Ms Gaidik appeared to be friendly at the first instance. It was a relief to know that they spoke and understood English fairly well. I thanked God for that silently as I would have dreaded to hear Rajeev's terrible translation.

As they joyfully wore their welcome garland made of bright yellow marigold flowers, they moved forward having a polite conversation with our Principal. The sight of the Maandna brought them to an abrupt standstill.

"What's that?" asked Jean Pierre, fascinated by the beautiful floor design.

Before any of us could utter a word, Gauransh broke into a long explanation, which left us astonished to no end.

"What you see before you is an exquisite example of the traditional floor designs called Maandna in Rajasthan, Rangoli in most parts of India and *Alpana* in few parts of India like West Bengal and Assam. The words Maandna Rangoli and Alpana are rooted in Vernacular languages and also have their origin in the Pre Aryan era. For example, Maandna in Rajasthani language literally means Mandan—to decorate. Rangoli, on the other hand, has its origin from the Sanskrit word *rangavalli*, which means a creeper drawn with colours. But the most interesting of them is Alpona or Alpana as it is popularly known... It is supposed that the root of this word is non-Aryan and is derived from the word *ailpona*, the art of making 'ails' or embankments. It was an art practiced because of the belief that these decorative paintings kept the dwelling, city or village safe and prosperous by magical representations of these designs."

We stared at Gauransh, our mouths agape.

"Wow!" said Gaidik, "That's wonderful information you gave us! I thought these were meaningless patterns drawn for beauty!"

"Certainly not!" exclaimed Gauransh indignantly, as though Gaidik had just made an insulting statement.

"In Rajasthan, based on appearance and regional applications, the designs revolve around the central motif which in its roots contains some geometric forms concerning a particular deity. The maandna designs of Rajasthan traditionally have close similarities with the geometric motifs like triangles, squares, circles, *swastikas* etc. There is a lot of Math involved here."

Gauransh paused to take a breath. When nobody stopped him from speaking, he continued with the same earnestness.

"What about Assam?" asked Gaidik.

"Assam is connected to Alpana or Alpona as many people say. You will be surprised to know that there are motifs in Alpana, of Bengal and neighbouring areas, which date back to the *Indus*

Valley Civilisation. The significant ones are fish with wings, conch, scorpion and Navagraha (the nine planets), amongst others," Gauransh concluded.

Gauransh had set the pace of our trip. Jean Pierre echoed our sentiments saying, "This trip promises to be a fabulous one!"

We all suddenly developed a lot of respect for Gauransh. He no longer appeared weird and funny to us. He was a genius indeed!

Chapter 2

THE CITY PALACE - OF ROYAL TALES & ANECDOTES

After the welcome and a brief tour of our school, it was decided to take the guests first to The City Palace.

"What is The City Palace? Is it the private residence of Princess Diya Kumari?" asked Jean Pierre.

"Yes," said Ms Kalpana Rai. "A segment of the palace is occupied by the Royal Family of Jaipur as their home. However, the major part of the palace complex is now a museum called Maharaja Sawai Man Singh II Museum. It is one of the most popular tourist spots in the city."

As we entered the gates of The City Palace, we were amused to see the visitors look awestruck at the huge entrance gates.

Gaidik exclaimed, "Good Lord! Why are these gates so huge?"

Priyamvada laughed aloud at their expressions and said in a very dramatic tone, "Welcome to Jaipur, folks." She then paused for a while and said, "My grandfather told me that most of the gates in and around The City Palace and further in the walled City are specially blessed to protect the citizens and the members of the Royal family from any harm. In fact, my great grandfather knew some old historians who quoted the city had been attacked time and

Udaipole Gate

again. But these gates, known as Pols, had such strong divine protection due to elaborate prayers and rituals done on each of them, that any attacking soldiers of the enemy camp would turn back mysteriously from the main gates of the city as they would not be able to enter. Till date nobody has been able to understand this phenomenon."

None of us realised that we had halted abruptly to hear Priyamvada's narrative.

"Wow!" said Gauransh and we all echoed his sentiments.

Suddenly, a lady approached us, dressed in kurta, jeans and sneakers.

"Hello, my name is Hema Rathore and I will be your guide for your entire stay in Rajasthan."

She gave a wide, friendly smile and continued, "I got a call from your school office to facilitate your tour."

Jean Pierre and Gaidik shook hands with Hema. She was a tall, robust personality with big, beautiful eyes and an ever smiling face.

We looked at each other silently, each having the same thought in mind. Hema caught the exchange of glances and said in a light, teasing voice, "So you did not expect a lady to join you as a guide?"

We all gave quick embarrassing denials. But the fact was that we were taken aback to see a lady guide. Although we had heard that there were a few of them around, yet we never expected to come across one. It is strange how we have a conditioned mindset about genders and occupations! I have yet to come across a lady postman, lady carpenters, plumbers, gardeners, lady mechanic… I couldn't think of more as I realised that women were now being seen in almost all fields of work.

"Gender stereotypes," Priyamvada whispered fiercely in my ears. "That is what we all are." I nodded in agreement.

"Shhh..." Meera said, "Just keep moving with her now."

Hema started speaking, "The City Palace is located in the center of Jaipur, near Jantar Mantar and Hawa Mahal. It is said that the ruler of Amer, Maharaja Sawai Jai Singh II, built the city of Jaipur in 1727 to meet the increasing need of population and water shortage. So he shifted his capital to Jaipur from Amer, which lies at a distance of 11 kilometres from Jaipur. The city of Jaipur was constructed under the supervision of his Minister Vidhyadhar Bhattacharya. The Maharaja himself designed The City Palace as well in accordance with the Vaastu shastra texts.

Gangapole

The City Palace of Jaipur is in the central northeast part of Jaipur city, the capital of Rajasthan. It incorporates an impressive and vast array of gardens, buildings and courtyards which are arranged in a linear series. It is a fusion of the Shilpa Shastra of Indian architecture with Rajput, Mughal, and European style of architecture," Hema Rathore paused to catch her breath. We all were following her, listening with rapt attention.

Old World Charm

"Also, you will be amazed to know that the linear alignment is not limited to the palace gardens, courtyards and buildings in the City Palace but extends even to the famous temple of Govind Devji, The Albert Hall Museum, and the Gadh Ganesh temple that you can see on top of that hill." Hema said pointing towards the white temple yonder.

Govind Dev ji

Gadh Ganesh

Bhuvan Misra sir further added an interesting piece of information, "The Gadh Ganesh temple is situated atop the Aravali hills. It was built by Maharaja Sawai Jai Singh II, when he performed the Ashvamedha Yajna before the establishment of Jaipur. The foundation stone of Jaipur was laid thereafter. The statue of Lord Ganesha which is placed inside the temple, is a unique one as it is Vigra Purushakriti—child Ganesha without the trunk. The Maharaja positioned the statue in such a way that he would be able to see it with the help of binoculars from the Chandra Mahal of The City Palace." We were fascinated to hear about the temple. Gaidik gasped aloud when Kalpana ma'am mentioned that one had to climb 365 stairs to reach the temple.

As we walked around through the various sections of the palace, I could not help but marvel at the fact that no matter how many times we may have seen the palace, yet, each trip always remained as exciting as always.

Silver Jars at Sarvatobhadra, The City Palace

All of a sudden, Miss Gaidik saw something and exclaimed, "Oh my God! This is a huge jar! Is it made of silver?"

Mr Bhuvan Mishra replied, "Yes, these silver urns are mentioned in the Guiness Book of World Record as the world's largest silver vessels."

"There is an interesting story behind these silver jars," said Hema. She continued, "The silver urns took two years to be made, between 1894 and 1896 CE. As per written records in Rajasthan State Archives, 42,000 silver coins were commissioned to make these urns. Each urn was made using 14,000 silver coins. So it is surmised that three such jars were crafted without being soldered at any point. So it is a unique, solid, single piece of jar."

"But, we see only two jars here, where is the third one?" quizzed Rajeev.

"As per written records, in 1902, the king, Maharaja Sawai Madho Singh II, had to attend the coronation ceremony of Prince Edward VII. Sawai Madho Singh was a highly pious Hindu and as per the Hindu belief prevalent at that time, he was not supposed to consume the water of any foreign land, across the seas. The priests told him that he could not go to England for this reason. Sawai Madho Singh was stumped as declining the invitation would have seemed very insulting.

Hence, it was finally decided to use the huge silver urns which were lying in the palace, to carry Ganga Jal or the holy water of the River Ganges, for the king to consume. It was also advised that a ship be found on which beef had never been cooked. Now, that was a very tall order indeed!" Hema paused.

"And then? Could they find such a ship?" I asked, thoroughly fascinated by the narrative.

"Yes," smiled Hema, "The SS Olympia apparently had not set sail ever before, hence it was selected for the royal voyage. It was prepared with elaborate prayers and rituals and more than 8000 litres of water was taken aboard in the silver jars. They came to be known as the Gangajalis."

"But what happened to the third silver jar? Did the king leave it in England?" asked Rajeev again.

"No, as per the legend (as there are no written records of this), the

Vintage Jaipur

king and his entourage encountered rough weather over the Red Sea. After consulting the priests, it was decided to toss one of the silver jars with all its holy water overboard to placate an angry Lord Varuna, the God of the oceans."

"Wow!" All of us chorused in unison.

We moved forward viewing the fascinating buildings, arches, domes and hearing equally fascinating facts about the history of the Palace and all the kings who had ruled the city of Jaipur. It was heartening to understand how progressive and far-sighted all the kings had been.

Chapter 2.1

PUTOLA BHAONA

As we came to the last portion of our tour, we heard some folk music and a rustic voice narrating something in hybrid Rajasthani, Hindi, and English language.

"Puppet show!" Rajeev exclaimed excitedly like a five-year-old kid.

"Where?" asked Jean Pierre with equal delight.

As we quickened our steps towards the sound, we reached an open space where we saw some cannons placed in the open. It looked an incongruous sight to see the set up of a puppet show amidst an array of cannons. Seeing two foreigners with us, the puppeteers called out to us loudly to see their next show.

A Puppet Show at the City Palace

"You must watch it," said Misra sir.

We weaved our way through a throng of visitors to see the puppet show closely.

"Look, Jean Pierre," Gaidik pointed excitedly towards the puppets on display. "How beautiful the peppy colours, sharp features and stylised eyes look!"

Jean Pierre agreed enthusiastically and we stayed on to see the amusing and entertaining show that was put up by the head puppeteer and his family.

"Can I talk to these artists?" asked Jean Pierre, once the show got over. "Could you help translate please, Ms Rai?"

What transpired was a very interesting and informative conversation between our visitors and the puppet artists. I knew a little bit about puppetry in Assam as my grandfather had told me a lot about it, and I waited eagerly for my turn to speak.

"Please tell us about puppetry in India and especially in Rajasthan. Is this specific only to your state?" translated Ms Rai in Hindi.

"Puppetry as an art has existed in India since more than a thousand years. And we are proud to say that Rajasthan is deemed to be the birthplace of this art. Although it is now a very popular art all across the country and abroad too," said Laxman, the main puppeteer.

"The puppet dance in Rajasthan is known as kathputli naach, as it is made up of two words, 'kaath' which means wood and 'putli' which means a lifeless doll," he paused to catch a breath. It seemed he was quite used to talking to visitors about this, as he narrated flawlessly.

"As per recorded history, putlibhats were the first people who discovered this art. They were specific tribes of Rajasthan who travelled to different villages, carrying their puppets and skills to entertain and educate the masses, in exchange of cash or barter of goods for their use. They soon gained popularity amongst the kings and received lavish patronage from them. The Bhat community settled in different kingdoms and got great appreciation and honour for their skill."

We listened with great interest. Then Gaidik asked, "What are the puppets made of?"

"They are made of mango wood and then stuffed with cotton and covered with highly embellished and colourful clothes. They are attached with a single string which passes from the top of the puppets over to the puppeteers. It requires a lot of practise and dexterity to wield the strings for the specific movements of the puppets," Laxman ended proudly.

We all clapped with glee. I could not help but pitch in my bit about the art of puppetry in Assam.

"May I share something from Assam about puppetry?" I asked hesitantly.

"Certainly!" said Gaidik enthusiastically.

"Well, this is something that my grandfather told me," I started. "The art of puppetry is extremely old in Assam. Some believe it goes back to the tenth century. The art of puppetry is quite similar in both the states. Even we have string puppets in Assam which are without legs, but people don't get to know because they are covered with long dresses. Like Rajasthani puppeteers, the Assamese puppeteers too narrate in a high pitch voice, using an instrument made of bamboo. It is called 'pepa'. The pitch is created by pressing the pepa in the middle of the puppeteer's lips," I continued speaking. "Formerly, the puppeteers of Assam were known as 'tatekia baazigar', but now the professional group of

puppeteers is known as ojha. In Assam, this art is not confined to any one community. It is practised by members of any religion or caste," I ended.

"And is it also known as kathputli over there?" asked Laxman.

"No, there it is known as putula naach or putola bhaona."

"What are the stories that are taken up by these puppeteers?" asked Jean Pierre.

"Well, usually stories from our ancient scriptures like Puranas are taken up or some popular myths and legends. However, nowadays, the puppeteers love to bring in popular western characters too, as part of their enactment," said Misra sir.

"Yes," said Rajiv, grinning, "I love it when they show Michael Jackson dancing."

We all laughed. Kalpana ma'am tipped Laxman and we moved ahead.

Chapter 3

AWESTRUCK BY JANTAR MANTAR

Our next stop was Jantar Mantar, which was in the vicinity of The City Palace. Well, actually, once upon a time, it had been a part of the palace itself. Now it is not only an astronomical observatory but is also a UNESCO World Heritage Site. We were excited to know that this

Jantar Mantar

monument which was completed in the year 1734, features the world's largest stone sundial.

"What does Jantar Mantar mean?" asked Jean Pierre.

"I know!" quipped Meera. "The word Jantar is derived from a Sanskrit word yantra meaning instrument or machine and mantar from Mantrana, which is also a Sanskrit word which means to consult, calculate. So it literally means "calculating instrument." She beamed, looking at Misra sir for a silent appreciation.

When we entered Jantar Mantar, we saw many architectural instruments which were huge and very beautifully constructed.

"Could you tell me, please, why would a king want to build an observatory?" asked Gaidik, perplexed seeing the huge stone and masonry instruments which varied in size from a few feet to 90 feet in height.

Hema smiled, "Very few people ask these questions. Well, to start with, Maharaja Sawai Jai Singh II was a brilliant astronomer, physicist, and mathematician with a deep knowledge of politics. One of his foremost objectives was to

Laghu Samrat Yantra

create astronomical instruments that would be more accurate and permanent than the brass instruments used at that time. He wished to make it really large. This decision of his resulted in creation of these huge structures for the measurement of celestial movement," she paused.

Hema started speaking again, "Maharaja Sawai Jai Singh II himself devised the Samrat Yantra, Jaya Prakash Yantra, and the Rama Yantra. The Samrat Yantra, also known as the Vrihat Samrat Yantra is the world's largest stone sundial. It is 27 meters high and is capable of measuring time to an accuracy of two seconds. Its shadow moves visibly at 1 mm per second, or roughly a hand's breadth, around 6 centimetres, every minute." Hema paused a while as we assimilated

Vrihat Samrat Yantra

the information. "The observatory consists of nineteen instruments for measuring time, predicting eclipses, tracking locations of major stars as The Earth orbits around The Sun, ascertaining the declinations of planets, and determining the celestial altitudes and related ephemerides," she concluded.

Gaidik said, "This is so impressive. I am eager to learn more about all the instruments and their uses."

Further, we saw many instruments and Hema explained each one of them.

The Unnatamsa Yantra (Unnat-elevated, Amsa-division, degree of arc) is an instrument that measures the altitude (the angular) height of an object in the sky.

The Chakra Yantra (Chakra-circle, Yantra- instrument) is a ring instrument which measures the global coordinates of declination and the hour angle of a celestial object.

Digmsa

Unnatamasa

Ram Yantra

Krantivritta Yantra

The Digamsa Yantra (Digamsa-azimuth) is a cylindrical instrument that has a simple method of determining the azimuth of a celestial object.

The Ram Yantra can measure the local coordinates of altitude and azimuth of a celestial object.

The Kranti Vritta Yantra—the use of this instrument is to find the declination and distance from the ecliptic and equinox of the sun and stars.

The Yantra Raj is an adaptation of an astrolabe—a medieval instrument for the measurement of time and the positions of celestial objects.

We heard everything with rapt attention. We also observed each instrument carefully and tried to do the things practically as much as we could.

We moved further to see the rest of the instruments.

"This is Rasivalaya or Zodiac Circle. These are instruments for measuring the celestial latitude and longitude of

Yantra Raj

Rasivalaya

the celestial bodies. There are twelve instruments which represent the twelve signs of the zodiac, one for each measurement to be done when the corresponding sign of the zodiac transits the meridian," said Hema.

We moved around awestruck. Every instrument was unique in itself and had a speciality which was sometimes difficult to comprehend. That gave me a thought, how exciting would it be to take up astronomy as a subject of study!

"Maharaja Sawai Jai Singh II built a total of five Jantar Mantars in India," said Hema, "at present only four Jantar Mantars exist, as the one at Mathura was torn down just before the first war of independence in 1857."

Gaidik asked, "Which was the largest observatory amongst all the Jantar Mantars?"

"The largest observatory amongst all the five is the one in Jaipur. In the olden days, it used to be the meeting point of different scientific cultures which gave rise to widespread social practices linked to cosmology," Hema concluded.

"We, the people of Rajasthan, respect our culture and heritage and that is why not only the government but the people also try to preserve our culture by taking care of these heritage sites," said Bhuvan sir.

Chapter 4

AHOM RAJA'S PALACE

The weather was very pleasant so we decided to walk down to our school. It was already evening and it had started turning dark. As we walked silently, trying to absorb all that we had seen, I suddenly realised that I had not shared anything about Assam since long. So I said, "Even the

Assamese people are very conscious about maintaining their heritage. The Assam government has preserved many heritage sites. Although Assam does not have as many forts and palaces as Rajasthan, yet, I would like to tell you about an ancient palace. It is not as huge as the City Palace but it is beautiful."

"We would love to hear about it," said Ms Kalpana Rai encouragingly.

"Well, let me share something about Ahom Raja's palace with you," I said.

"It is a seven-storeyed building and was built by King Suklenmung, the king of Ahom Kingdom. The palace is situated in Gargaon, the capital of Ahom which is presently known as Sivasagar town."

"It is also called the Gargaon Palace and it has a history of 250 years. I find two things very unique about this palace," I paused.

"The first is that the King ordered the palace to be built with impermanent materials like wood and stones. I think

it was constructed somewhere around 1540 CE. After some time, a brick wall and masonry gateway was constructed in the capital complex by King Pramatta Singha. King Rajeshwar Singha further contributed in the designing of the mansion which gives it an elegant look. He is the one who completed the palace in 1752 CE and gave it the look that you see today." I paused again.

"And, the second thing?" questioned Gauransh curiously.

I smiled, "Believe it or not but eggs and rice were used to make the mortar for the construction of this monument rather than any cement."

Everybody gasped to my utter delight.

We reached our school. There was a vehicle waiting to transport our guests to the hotel. We bid farewell for the day and each returned home, geared up excitedly for the next day's tour around the city of Jaipur.

Chapter 5

A PEEK INTO THE PINK CITY - LORD KRISHNA'S CROWN

Albert Hall

The next day we all gathered in the school premises, excitedly looking forward to a day out in the city. Hema had gone to pick up our guests and on her way to the school, she showed them the Albert Hall Museum. Jean Pierre was excited to see the Albert Hall Museum and shared what he had learnt about it.

"It is considered to be the oldest museum of the State and is situated in Ram Niwas Garden. It was designed by Samuel Swinton Jacob in Neo-Mughal-Hindu style architecture with

Rajput influences. The foundation of the museum was laid down in the year 1876 when Albert Edward, the Prince of Wales, visited Jaipur."

Gaidik added, "I just read that Rudyard Kipling, the famous British poet, was so astounded by the aura and architectural magnificence of the Albert Hall that he wrote, 'It is now a rebuke to all other museums in India from Calcutta downwards'."

"That's quite a compliment," I said, giving a thumbs up sign.

"Did you see the mummy there?" Meera asked excitedly.

"Yes," laughed Jean Pierre.

"Do you know the story behind the pink colour of Jaipur?" We all shook our heads. "As per a popular story, the whole city was painted pink to welcome Queen Victoria's son, Prince Albert Edward, and ever since, Jaipur has been called The Pink City. This happened during the reign of Maharaja Sawai Ram Singh II."

"Why pink?" asked Priyamvada. "I always wondered why this unusual colour was chosen."

"The colour chosen was terracotta pink as this colour represents warmth and hospitality," Hema answered.

Jean Pierre was excited to know more about Jaipur and why it is every traveller's delight. According to him each place has a history of its own and the stories, legends, and myths make it even more special. He wanted to be acquainted with what Jaipur offers to all the visitors. He asked Gauransh what makes Jaipur the top choice of travellers.

Gauransh delightfully answered, "Our city is an essential part of Rajput history and has a lot to offer in terms of culture, activities and sightseeing."

Meera broke in between, "Jaipur is all about culture, heritage, hospitality, and the colour pink."

Both Jean Pierre and Gaidik seemed super excited to embark on the journey.

Soon we set off to visit all the iconic attractions of Jaipur.

Our first halt was none other than the Hawa Mahal.

Jaipur's most-distinctive landmark, the Hawa Mahal is an extraordinary pink-painted, delicately honeycombed hive that rises a dizzying five storeys. Hawa Mahal is also called The Palace of Winds.

Since it is located at a stone's throw distance from our school, it just took us five minutes to reach there.

As expected, the French delegates were ready with their line of queries, which we all were eager to answer as we explored this wonderful palace.

Gaidik said, "Tell us something about its history."

Priyamvada was the first one to reply, "In 1799, the Kachhwaha Rajput ruler, Maharaja Sawai Pratap Singh, grandson of Maharaja Sawai Jai Singh II, ordered Lal Chand Ustad to construct an extension to the Royal City Palace."

Jean Pierre asked, "What is the meaning of Hawa Mahal?"

Meera answered, "The word 'Hawa' means wind or breeze and 'Mahal' is a palace. So Hawa Mahal is The Palace of Winds."

Gauransh was eager to pour out his account of facts and wanted to explain why it was built. He said, "The Purdah system at that time was strictly followed. Rajput royal ladies could not be seen by strangers or appear in any public area. The construction of Hawa Mahal allowed the royal ladies to enjoy day-to-day street scenes and royal processions on the street without being seen." Gauransh gave a quick glance towards Hema as though to confirm whether he had spoken correctly. Hema gave an approving smile.

"That sounds interesting!" said Gaidik.

Gauransh added, "Do you know that Hawa Mahal has no foundation?"

Everyone including me was wonderstruck to hear this.

"That's correct," Hema said. "Hawa Mahal was built without any foundation. In fact, it is the tallest building in the world without a foundation. The five-storeyed building managed to remain upright because it is curved in shape. It is one of the masterpieces of Rajput and Mughal architecture."

Rajeev was there to share what he knew. He said, "The Mahal has a total of 953 small casements each with small lattice work, pink windows called jharokhas, balconies, and arched roofs with hanging cornices."

The French teachers wanted to know why so many windows had been made.

Hema explained, "There were two purposes for the seemingly excessive number of windows. First, these

Reminiscing the Hawa Mahal

windows offered a beautiful glimpse of street life to the royal ladies ensconced in the palace. Secondly, they allowed the breeze to flow through which kept the palace cool. It thus made it an ideal summer palace. It was a summer retreat for the royal families during olden times."

Gaidik asked, "What is it made of?"

Gauransh answered, "Hawa Mahal is built of lime and mortar with additional cladding of red and pink sandstone. And one more interesting fact related to this masterpiece is that this five-storeyed palace was built in the form of Lord Krishna's crown because Maharaja Sawai Pratap Singh had been a pious devotee of Lord Krishna, the Hindu God."

Everything about Hawa Mahal was so fascinating and absorbing that it became difficult for us to move ahead. Had it not been for Hema, we would never have made it to our next destination on time, ever.

Chapter 5.1

OF FAIRS & FESTIVALS

We settled in our vehicle that would take us to the Jaigarh and Nahargarh Forts. Jean Pierre casually asked, "Which is the most popular festival of Rajasthan?" Before anyone could even register the query in their minds, pat came the reply from Gauransh, 'Teej'.

Priyamvada said defiantly, "I disagree. I think it's Gangaur."

"Well, let's see," quipped Gauransh. "Teej festival is one of its kinds. There are three types of Teej: Hariyali, Kajau/ Kajli and Hartalika. Jaipur's celebration of Hariyali Teej is an event to watch out for. The grand two-day procession has a finely decorated idol of Teej Mata, Goddess Parvati, in a royal palanquin. It starts from Tripolia Gate and after passing through various markets with lots of traditional dances, songs and folk artists showcasing their performances, the procession ends at Chaugan Stadium."

"The finely decked up elephants, horses, and camels are a sight to behold," added Hema.

"And don't you girls like to put intricate mehndi on your palms, just like your mothers at home," added Rajeev with a teasing expression, pointing at me and Priyamvada.

"Is this mehndi, the famous Henna art of India?" asked Gaidik excitedly, extending her palm as if in anticipation of some mehndi design to appear magically on her palm.

Now it was Meera's turn to add on to the fact train so well crafted by Gauransh.

She said, "Yes, mehndi is the Henna art and on Teej, the women decorate their hands and get dressed in ethnic attire to worship Goddess Parvati to seek her blessings for marital bliss. The festivities also include swings, songs, adorning of traditional jewelry, and specific sweets such as Ghevar, Malpua, and Besan Sattu as the festival celebrates the reunion of Lord Shiva and Goddess Parvati after 108 rebirths of Sati."

To this Priyamvada added, "Similarly, Gangaur is celebrated to seek the blessings from Lord Shiva and Goddess Parvati for marital bliss. Unmarried women observe fast for seeking a good husband and married women pray for their husband's good health, wealth and prosperity. Gangaur, the word itself stands for the union of two people– 'Gana' means Lord Shiva and 'Gauri' means Goddess Gauri–

another name of Goddess Parvati .This festival too is celebrated with a grand procession that starts from Zenani Deodhi, the women's courtyard at The City Palace and reaches Talkatora after passing through various busy markets of the Walled City. The festival is a sixteen-day affair during which the women observe fast every day, eating only one meal a day. On the last three days the idols of deities are decorated with ornaments and beautiful dresses. The married women carry the idols of these deities on their head in local processions. On the final day, the idols are immersed into the water, bidding farewell to Goddess Gauri. It indicates sending Gauri to her consort's house and therefore, the married women also return to their husband's house after celebrating Gangaur at their parent's house."

Gaidik and Jean Pierre uttered a "WOW!" in unison.

Gaidik then turned to me and asked, "Isn't there a colourful procession on one of the festivals of Assam too?"

"Yes! It is the festival of Me–Dam–Me–Phi," I replied. "The colourful cultural procession taken out on this occasion is marked by people singing songs, dressed in traditional

Assamese attire. The practice of ancestor worship is embodied in the Me-Dam-Me-Phi festival of Assam which is celebrated on 31 January every year." I paused to gather my thoughts and to recall some more details. "The story of Me-Dam-Me-Phi is connected with the arrival of the Tai people in Assam and founding of the Ahom kingdom that would rule till the advent of the British. The Tai people who settled in Assam were henceforth called 'Ahoms', a word derived from 'asama' or 'invincible' in local language. Interestingly even the name of the region 'Assam' has the same origins. The Ahoms had a custom of making offerings to ancestors as the Tai-Ahoms believed that their deceased ancestors were still with them in the form of spirits. The offerings are a way to renew the connection with ancestors on occasions such as Me-Dam-Me-Phi. This literally translates as Me–offering, Dam– ancestors and Phi-gods," I paused once again to catch my breath and continued to speak after composing my thoughts.

"Earlier in the late 17th century, it used to be an elite ceremony performed only by the king to avert imminent danger, commemorate a victory, or seek longevity. However, now it is celebrated by the community at large although it stays as an intimate affair for most families who perform rituals

in the privacy of their own homes. The offering includes homemade wine, rice, and various preparations of fish and meat. The offerings are placed on a specially constructed layered platform called mehenga which is made of bamboo, banana stalk, and banana leaves." I continued, "Another well-known festival of Assam is Bihu. And Gauransh as you said there are three types of Teej, so are there three types of Bihu- Rongali Bihu or Bohag Bihu is celebrated in the month of April, Kaati Bihu in October and Bhogali Bihu, also called Magh Bihu, is celebrated in the month of January."

"Why so many Bihus?" asked Gaidik, looking confused.

"Each Bihu has its own significance. Rongali Bihu is the festival of merriment and ushers in the Assamese New Year. This is the most popular amongst all Bihus and is celebrated with much joy. Bhogali Bihu, also called the Magh Bihu, is a harvest festival and then we have the Kati Bihu which is a sombre, thrifty one signifying shortage of supplies. Kaati Bihu is also called Kongali Bihu. The word Kongali means poor and refers to a time of poor supplies. During this time, special kinds of lamps called Akaxh Banti or the sky candles are lit near the paddy fields. These lamps are lit high on the tips of high bamboos to appease the Gods so that the fields may be blessed with a good harvest."

"Interesting," mumbled Jean Pierre. "Is this connected to their religious beliefs?"

"Yes, but it also has a scientific reason behind it," I answered. "The lamps attract the insects that eat the crop and harm them. The insects fall prey to the flames of the lamp, thereby keeping the crops safe."

"Ingenious!" exclaimed Gaidik.

"Are there any dances and festivities for young people also during Bihu? I wish I could go there to freak out," Rajeev said with a twinkle in his eye.

"Yes, of course!" I exclaimed, "During this time, the young people in the villages may be seen moving about in groups gaily dressed or forming circles in the midst of which the prettiest girls dance, singing songs of love and romance. Such gatherings are called Mukoli Bihus (Open Bihus). The songs are very popular among all sections of the people. Dear Rajeev, you must visit Assam at this time," I said humorously.

"Nowadays, Mukoli Bihus are not common any more. In towns and cities, there are well-organized Bihu fairs where professional or amateur troupes perform Bihu songs and dance on stage. People during this time, get in their best traditional attire. The tune of traditional musical instruments including Toka Xutuli, Baanhi, Dhol and Gogona, add a different kind of flavour in the atmosphere," I added with a chuckling sound.

"Oh! If Mukoli Bihus are no longer common, why are you so keen to pack me off to Assam?" said Rajeev with mock indignation. Every body smiled.

"I wish we plan a trip to Assam very soon," said Gaidik.

"Yes," agreed Jean Pierre.

"Maybe I can join too!" I said.

"Me too," echoed Priyamvada and Meera together to which Rajeev added, "And you will need me and Gauransh as the best source of all information about Assam and its culture. We promise we won't charge a penny."

Everyone laughed aloud.

Chapter 5.2

THE FORTS

Our vehicle was soon winding its way up the hills. As we neared Nahargarh, we could see our visitors getting excited to get out and explore.

Hema started speaking, "This is the famous Nahargarh Fort which was originally named Sudarshangarh. Nahargarh means abode of tigers."

Located in one of the oldest mountain ranges of the world, the Aravalis , the Nahargarh Fort was built in 1734 by Maharaja Sawai Jai Singh II, founder of Jaipur."

Our guests seemed to be captivated by the breathtaking view of the scenic surroundings. As we entered the fort through the entrance gate called 'Tadigate', we saw a temple dedicated to the rulers of Jaipur.

"Isn't the architecture of the fort Indo-European?" inquired Gaidik.

View of Nahargarh Fort from the Palace School, Jaipur

"Yes indeed, you are absolutely correct." Hema replied promptly.

Priyamvada, who had been very quiet on the way due to motion sickness, now remarked that there was another temple devoted to the Rathore prince, Nahar Singh Bhomia inside the fort.

"Yes, and if stories are to be believed, the construction of this fort was stopped by the spirit of the Rathore Prince and it was only when a temple dedicated to him was built inside the fort that the spirit was pacified," added Gauransh.

"That sounds incredible!" exclaimed Jean Pierre.

"I have also read somewhere that the fort was renovated in the year1868 under the reign of Maharaja Sawai Ram Singh, who was also known as the Photographer Prince," said Priyamvada.

"Yes," Hema confirmed and further added, "This fort was also known to be the favourite hunting point of the Maharajas once upon a time."

As we walked through the magnificent fort, we came upon an area which seemed to be having more visitors than the other parts of the fort. In fact I became quite curious to know what was happening there as people seemed to be buying tickets and moving further ahead. Jean Pierre pointed and remarked, "This area looks different from the other areas of the fort, is there anything special?"

"This area has been allocated to the Jaipur Wax Museum and the Sheesh Mahal," answered Hema. "It was built with the support of the Department of Archaeology and Museums, Jaipur, Department of Tourism, and Government of Rajasthan." This was news to me too. I was not aware that our city had a wax museum.

"You will be happy to know that the museum uses solar power to meet its electricity needs. The solar power project has not only reduced the electricity bill but is also helping to reduce the carbon footprints," Hema informed us with pride.

"What is the Sheesh Mahal?" I asked. Hema smiled, "Ah, the Sheesh Mahal! This place needs to be seen to understand its beauty and appreciate the fine Rajasthani craftsmanship." Our guests showed keen interest in seeing the Sheesh Mahal. Our excitement knew no bounds as none of us had seen it.

I was awestruck by the sheer beauty and grandeur of the Sheesh Mahal which is also known as The Palace of Mirrors. It is a new landmark of Jaipur which has been designed with 25 million glass pieces with thikri, mirror work and gold polish giving a magnificent royal look and feel.

"Twenty-five million glass pieces! Unbelievable!" exclaimed Jean Pierre as we moved out of the Sheesh Mahal. We all were wonderstruck indeed.

The tour of the fort brought us to yet another interesting point.

"Another very interesting feature in the fort is its water harvesting system," said Hema as she made us walk towards the huge step well. She continued, "The extensive water system of Nahargarh is one of the most significant features of the fort. The catchment area of water for Nahargarh extends to about 6 kms surrounding the fort."

Gauransh couldn't help but add to the interesting narrative by Hema. He looked it up on his tab and continued, "A network of six closed catchments connects through small canals and aqueducts and drains are laid in and outside the fort. Small canals bring rainwater from the higher reaches of the hills. The bed of these canals is designed in such a way that it is on a gradient and also at the same time has an undulating course. Nahargarh has two large step wells called Baolis and a smaller step well called Kund. The step wells receive water from the catchment in the surrounding hills while the Kund receives rainwater harvested from the fort complex."

"The famous song 'Masti Ki Pathshala' from the movie *Rang De Basanti,* was shot right here," said Priyamvada, pointing to the walls of the step well in an overly dramatic manner.

I nodded with a smile, knowing fully well, what a big Bollywood fan Priyamvada was.

Hema added, "That movie made this step well a big tourist attraction. Not only do the people enjoy the scenic beauty of this place but they also end up appreciating the ingenuity of the local people in the bygone era. In Jaisalmer you will get to learn more about the indigenous water harvesting systems of Rajasthan."

We all were ecstatic to see the magnificent Nahargarh Fort.

Nahargarh Stepwell

Our next halt was the Jaigarh Fort, and Hema enlightened us with its history.

"The fort is located on The Hill of Eagles or cheel ka teela as it is locally known. It was built by Sawai Jai Singh II in 1726 and was named after him. The fort is also known as Victory Fort. It has a length of three kilometres and a width of one kilometre."

She further added, "The main entrance of the fort is called the Dungar Darwaza. There are two ancient temples in the fort, one is the Ram Harihar temple of the 10th century and the other is the Kal Bhairav temple of the 12th century."

"So these temples are older than the forts," remarked Gaidik. Hema nodded and continued, "The fort is highly fortified and has huge thick walls made up of red sandstone. There are several beautiful palaces such as Laxmi Niwas Palace, Lalit Mandir Palace, Vilas Mandir Palace, and Aram Mandir Palace within the fort.

After walking for some time Jean Pierre asked if the fort was a residential one. To this Priyamvada quickly responded that it was not a residential fort but was an artillery production unit of the Rajputs.

"I have also heard that the Jaigarh Fort was built to overlook and protect the Amber Fort of Jaipur," remarked Meera.

"Yes, it was actually the main defensive structure. The Jaigarh fort and Amber Fort are connected with sub surface passages," said Hema, "also, due to the abundance of iron ore mines near the fort, the Jaigarh Fort became one of the richest cannon foundries of its time."

As we walked further, Gaidik and Jean Pierre were very excited to see the world's largest wheeled cannon 'Jai Vaan' about which they had heard from Rajeev. The cannon had been fired only once with a charge of 100 kilograms (220 lb.) of gunpowder and when fired covered a distance of about 35 kilometres.

Jean Pierre looked very surprised and asked, "Why was it used just once?"

"Maybe its mere presence and public knowledge of the damage it could inflict, prevented its usage," Meera said with a smile.

"What about the water supply of this fort?" questioned Gaidik.

Jai Vaan Cannon

"Water was supplied from Sagar Lake which was artificially created. Water from Sagar Lake used to be transported to the fort in pouches loaded on elephant backs and also by humans carrying water pots. The water used to be stored in three underground tanks below the central courtyard. One tank was used to store water, second was rumoured to have stored gold and jewellery, while the third was supposedly empty," informed Gauransh with a twinkle in his eye, for he knew he had just spoken of a legendary rumour.

"It is truly amazing to see how and what the old maharajas and their minions did hundreds of years ago. Life was truly difficult but it is heartening to see that almost all of them had efficient systems in place to deal with every kind of situation," observed Gaidik.

Jean Pierre and Gaidik were not only captivated by the structure and history of both the forts but were also impressed with the water management system they had observed in both the places.

"And do you know what fascinated me the most?" asked Rajeev. We looked at him questioningly, "These huge halls of audience which we see in most forts, they intrigue me. We have been told that these huge areas were used by the kings to address their subjects or their soldiers and military commanders."

"So?" Hema asked, unable to understand what was intriguing about it.

"So, my question is, how did they address large gatherings without any mics and speakers? How were they audible?"

We looked at him, surprised. This had not occurred to any one of us.

Jean Pierre said thoughtfully, "It has something to do with the acoustics, I think. It is evident that ancient architecture was extremely advanced in many ways. I am sure they kept acoustics in mind while constructing."

"Quite possible..." Rajeev's voice trailed off. With this thought to ponder upon, we decided to move towards Amber Fort.

Chapter 5.3

MYSTERIOUS TUNNELS AND PASSAGEWAYS

"Where do we go next, Hema?" Meera asked.

"Amber Fort or Amer as it is popularly known in Jaipur. It is yet another UNESCO World Heritage Site," smiled Hema.

Rajeev said, "Let me call the driver to get the vehicle ready."

"NO!" Hema said sharply. We looked at her surprised. She gave an embarrassed laugh and said, "We will walk down to Amber Palace. Ask him to wait for us at the Amber Palace parking lot."

I gasped and so did the others, "Walk down!" We chorused in dismay.

"It is a long, treacherous and an arduous walk!" said Ms Rai.

"Actually, we will walk down an ancient tunnel," said Hema thoroughly enjoying the look of dismay on our faces.

"Are you serious?" Rajeev asked incredulously.

"Yes!" Hema laughed loudly. "Let's go!"

We followed her, feeling like mice scurrying behind the Pied Piper of Hamelin.

We soon arrived at the old, mysterious looking entry of the tunnel. A blast of cold breeze hit us as we entered it. Hema began her narrative, "This ancient 18th century undercover path connects the Jaigarh Fort and the Amber Palace. It is approximately a 325 metre long cobbled pathway which was used by the erstwhile rulers. One can either walk or take a battery operated golf cart. What do you prefer?"

"We would prefer to walk," said Jean Pierre.

"Ok. So let's go!"

I felt shivers go down my spine as we entered the dimly lit, cold, narrow passageway.

"It is actually an open air tunnel. It is believed that the pathway was constructed as a defence mechanism so that in case of an attack on Amber Palace, members of the royal family and others could be evacuated undetected

Amer Wall

from the Palace to the Fort. The Jaigarh Fort is thus constructed at a higher level on the mountain, compared to the Amber Palace."

"How long does it take to reach Amber?" asked Bhuvan Misra sir.

"Well, depending on your speed of walking, it can take you anything from 25 to 40 minutes. If you travel by car, the Palace would be around 7 kilometres away," Hema answered.

Soon, we were out in the open. I felt as if we were a part of beautifully painted scenery. There was an imperceptible haze around us which gave the entire view a mysterious look. On one hand we could see the Jaigarh Fort behind us and on the other hand, walking further ahead, we suddenly came upon a breathtaking view of the Amber Palace.

The tawny-coloured Amber Palace lay in front of us, sprawled over the hill in resplendent beauty. We could see the Maota, a manmade lake, brimming with water. It was complemented beautifully by the Kesar Kyari Bagh (garden) in its midst.

"This is a sight to behold!" said Gaidik with a catch in her voice.

"Yes," Jean Pierre agreed, "I am struck by how unbelievably visual this place is!"

Gaidik looked at us and remarked, "This long length of wall running along reminds me of the Great Wall of China."

Gauransh quickly added something which none of us had been aware of, "You will be surprised to know that actually this is one of the longest walls in the world. Some say it is the third longest wall but that is debatable. However, the fact remains that the Amber Wall is really long. The government is trying to restore it slowly. Unfortunately, due to the ravages of time, a major part of the wall has crumbled away."

"Gaidik, doesn't this cobbled pathway remind you of some ancient castles we have visited in Europe?" Jean Pierre asked.

Gaidik nodded enthusiastically.

Chapter 5.4

THE GLORIOUS AMBER FORT

We walked on in silence, soaking the beauty of the place. Soon we were inside the Amber Palace.

Our guide took over as we walked around one of the most beautiful forts situated in the Aravali hills.

"The Amer Fort is situated in Amber, 11 kilometres from Jaipur and is one of the most famous forts of Rajasthan. Amer, originally was the capital of this State before Jaipur.

The kingdom was known as Dhundar. Amer had been ruled by

the Kachhwahas from the 11th to the 16th century, until the capital was moved from here to Jaipur. Raja Man Singh I built this fort in the year1592 AD and Raja Jai Singh I expanded and renovated it later. While many such old structures have been either destroyed or replaced by other things, this fort has stood against all the tests of time and invasions."

We walked up to the point where once again, we came upon the Kesar Kyari Garden and the Maota Lake.

"This garden with these geometric shapes is almost anachronistic," remarked Gaidik.

"Actually, yes, now that you mention it, this garden does not seem to belong to a bygone era. Nestled below the rugged hills and barren terrain, it is striking because of its man-made dammed lake, square platform base, stepped terraces and patterned planting. It is in stark contrast to the rugged historic backdrop," said Hema. "But there was a reason for constructing this garden. It was created in 1600 CE for the women of the royal entourage to admire from high above. According to Tom Turner, a renowned garden historian and landscape architect, there was also

Kesar Kyari

The Amer Fort

an ingenious pulley system here that allowed the women to reach the garden directly from their rooms, thereby avoiding any inappropriate contact with males enroute. And apart from this, the Maota was created to gather rain water as this was the main source of water for the inhabitants of the fort."

We moved on, enjoying the view of various areas demarcated for different purposes in the fort like the public hall of audience, the private residence for the queens and many more interesting areas. We were delighted to see the original Sheesh Mahal which is a marvellous example of Thikri, the famous mirror inlay world of Rajasthan. The Sheesh Mahal of Amer is believed to have been built in the sixteenth century unlike the modern version at Nahargarh fort which has been built in the twenty first century. Both have their own unique charm and unparalleled beauty. Gaidik and Jean Pierre were completely bowled over when Hema lit a candle and twirled around gently, making the flickering candle flame reflect in all the glass pieces, dancing as though part of an orchestrated performance. It transported us back to the bygone days. No, doubt it was one of the most beautiful forts that I had ever seen.

We soon came upon the powerful temple of Shila Mata.

Chapter 5.5

THE LEGEND OF SHRI SHILA DEVI TEMPLE

"And now we have arrived at one of the most revered temples of our State-Shila Mata temple. Would you like to listen to the fascinating tale about its inception?" asked Hema.

We nodded our heads eagerly. It was decided that we would first go inside the temple to pay our respects to the deity and then listen to the folklore while moving out of the fort. We were tired and hungry and wanted to eat something soon. Our last stop for the day was another exciting outing I had never had- night safari in the Jhalana Forest Reserve.

Shri Shila Mata

As we were on our way back moving towards our vehicle after

paying obeisance at the temple of Shri Shila Mata at Amer, Priyamvada shared an interesting piece of information which made all of us from The Palace School feel very proud. She told us that the Shri Shila Mata temple was looked after and maintained by the Shri Shila Mata Temple Trust which was headed by none other than the Chairperson of our school Her Highness Rajmata Padmini Devi ji of Jaipur. It was interesting to note the sense of pride and belongingness we all experienced upon hearing this.

As soon as we settled into our vehicle, Hema began her riveting narrative about the legend of Shri Shila Devi.

"Towards the end of the 16th century, Maharaja Mansingh brought the statue of the Goddess Shila Mata from the eastern part of Bengal. In the kingdom of Pratapaditya, Maharaja Man Singh received a defeat at the hands of King Kedar. Depressed, the Maharaja worshipped Goddess Kali who appeared in his dream and blessed him which changed his defeat into victory. The Goddess also obtained a promise from the Maharaja that he would establish her shrine in his capital. The idol of the Goddess was recovered from the sea in the form of a Shila (slab) and it was brought to Amer. When cleaned and washed, the present idol appeared. This is why the Goddess is named as Shila Mata."

"Fascinating," murmured Gaidik.

Hema continued speaking about the temple as we cruised towards our luncheon destination, a traditional Rajput house called The Haveli.

"The temple belongs to the Shakti cult of Hindus who worship Goddess Durga in her many forms. It took ten years to build this temple. Every year during the months of April and October, Hindus celebrate nine holy days of prayers and fasting called the Navratri. This temple draws lakhs of devotees from all over the city, state and beyond, who throng the temple to pray in front of their revered deity. People are known to walk miles and miles as a form of pilgrimage to please the Goddess and seek her blessings."

Hema's narration was halted midway by a loud shriek in the vehicle, "My purse!" It was Gaidik.

"What happened?" we asked simultaneously.

"My purse is missing! It had my passport and all my money!" Gaidik was panic stricken. We also got alarmed.

"Did you drop it somewhere?" asked Jean Pierre.

"I don't know!" she said, looking utterly dismayed. "I remember I had it when we were moving out of the Jaigarh Fort. I slung it on my shoulder… after that I don't remember anything."

Ms Rai advised them to report the matter to the police and also if required, inform the embassy thereafter. All our exuberance vanished in thin air. We alighted from the vehicle very quietly upon reaching The Haveli. Hema ushered us inside and told us to have our lunch. Meanwhile, she made a few calls to the Amer and the Jaigarh Fort offices as well as to somebody she knew in the police department.

We freshened up quickly in a somber mood. The owner of The Haveli told us to take a look around his abode till the time the food was laid down on the table.

Chapter 5.6

ART TALKS - INDIAN MONA LISA

We were led around The Haveli by a middle aged gentleman named Ranveer Sisodia. He took us on a tour around the property, which was replete with old paintings, antiques and rare artefacts from all over the country. Gaidik, though a bit distracted, seemed to be enjoying the ambience. I often saw her turn around, searching for Hema and then turn back a bit disappointed as she seemed to be nowhere around us.

We were enthralled by the beautifully carved artworks with eye-catching combinations of colors from different areas, showing the creative genius of the local artists.

Mr Ranveer Sisodia made a very pertinent remark, "Art not only depicts the personality of the people of specific regions but also gives an insight into the culture and history of the area. There are so many artforms present in our country and each one has a different story to tell about their culture and their people."

Jean Pierre looked bewildered, "How is that possible?"

"Excuse me," we heard Hema's voice "Good news for you, Gaidik!" she called out with a smile. "Your purse has been found and is now being delivered here at The Haveli."

It was good to see the wave of relief and joy on Gaidik's face. We too felt very happy for her.

"Where did they find it?" enquired Gaidik.

"Apparently, you dropped it while clicking pictures of the open air tunnel entrance at Jaigarh. There was a young urchin close by who saw it lying on the ground. He often wanders there in search of tips and food. He turned it over at the ticket counter."

"How honest!" we all exclaimed.

"He could have easily taken the money and vanished. But he didn't!" Gaidik spoke in wonder. "I would like to reward him please. How do I contact him? Can he come along with the person who is bringing my purse back to me?"

Hema assured her that she would do the needful and told her to continue with the tour.

We resumed our interesting conversation with Mr Sisodia.

"You wanted to know how art can reveal the history and culture of a region didn't you?" Mr Sisodia asked Jean Pierre. Seeing Jean Pierre nod his head, Mr Sisodia said, "Well, let me give you an example. What you see in front of you is a beautiful piece of Bani Thani painting. You will be amused to know that this particular piece is also called Indian Mona Lisa. This beautiful lady in the portrait is actually from the Kishangarh Miniature Bani Thani School of Art. Miniature paintings were first introduced in India between the 9-10th century during the Buddhist Pala period and represented the way of living in that period of time. However, it was under the Mughal rule between 16th to 18th century that this style of painting flourished. Rajputs were also great admirers of art. With the decline of the Mughal dynasty, many of the Mughal court painters sought employment under the Rajput kings. The paintings thus made under the Rajput rule had a deep influence of Mughal art style. However, they differed in colour and themes used."

We all listened quietly. For us, as students, this was a new perspective towards art.

"Why the name Bani Thani?" asked Meera.

Mr Sisodia smiled, "Ah! There is a reason behind that!"

"The Rajasthani paintings were divided into different schools, one of which was the Kishangarh School of Art. Artists created beautiful, intricate paintings under the rule of Maharaja Savant Singh, an 18th century Rajput ruler. He was a devotee of Lord Krishna hence most paintings were inspired from stories of Lord Krishna and Radha. In fact, Radha-Krishna depicted in the paintings, represented Maharaja Savant Singh and his wife Vishnupriya whom he deeply loved. Vishnupriya, adorned herself with exquisite makeup and jewelry to represent her royal stature, as she had been a court singer before becoming the king's consort. Her elegant style got her the name Bani Thani (or a well-decked woman)," Mr Sisodia ended with a broad smile.

Indian Mona Lisa

"Fascinating," Gaidik murmured and we found ourselves saying the same.

"Apart from that, the Rajasthani tradition is also incorporated in the portraits. Bani Thani is dressed like a bride with traditional Rajasthani sheer odhni or long scarf that covers half of her face like a veil. This veil is the cultural symbol of a woman's modesty and honour. The woman is bedecked with traditional pieces of jewellery. The artworks under the Rajputs, had a religious character, which is why it is believed that Bani Thani's portrait was inspired by Radha's figure. Bani Thani figures would often have a lotus bud in the hands, symbolising purity and divinity. Gradually, all female characters in the paintings came to be called Bani Thani."

Chapter 5.7

ART TALKS – LUNCH BREAK!

Lunch was an elaborate affair with Rajasthani cuisine served traditionally on the floor with cushions arranged in two parallel lines, facing each other. The visitors were fascinated by the way daal, baati, choorma, khato, mirch ke tapore, gatte ki sabzi, lehsun ki chutney, kair sangri, pickle, and rice were served personally by the hosts to all the guests. They

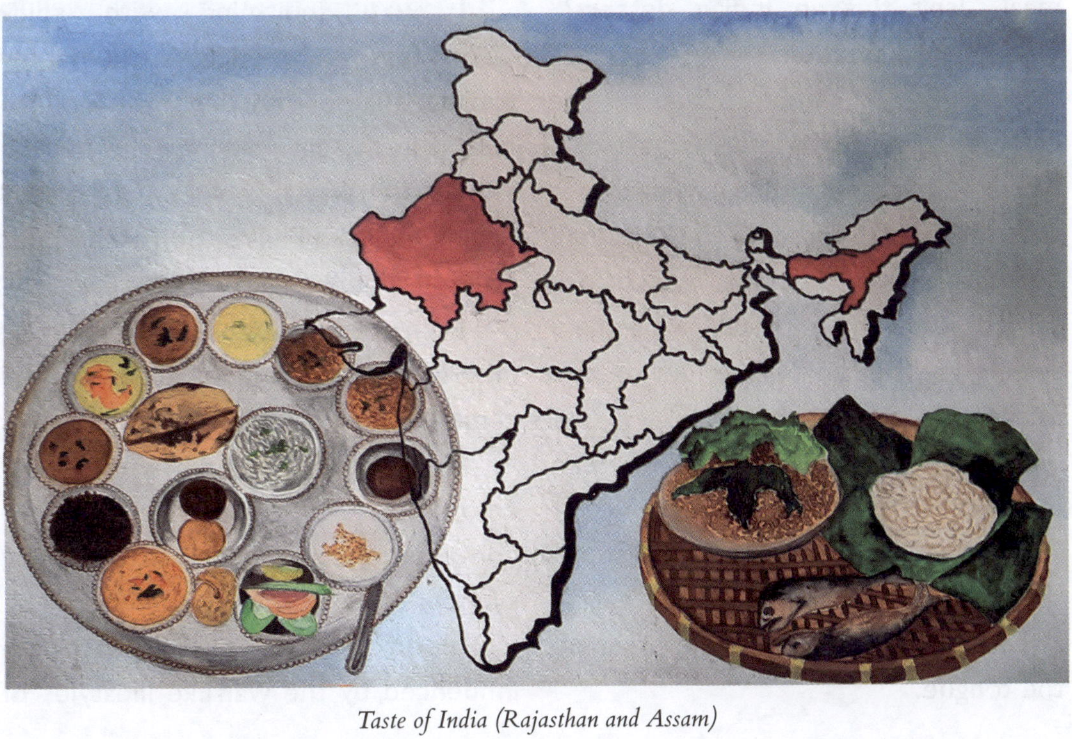

Taste of India (Rajasthan and Assam)

Rajasthani Cuisine

were mystified to see gulab jamun, being served as a starter to the main meal. "Isn't this an Indian dessert?" Gaidik asked, puzzled.

"Serving sweets at the commencement of a meal is part of a typical Rajasthani culture. Sweet dishes are not called desserts in Rajasthan because unlike desserts, which are served after the meal, Rajasthani sweets are served before, during and after meals," Meera smiled.

"But why?" asked Jean Pierre bewildered.

"Probably because the food is super spicy," said Bhuvan Misra sir, "eating sweets in between takes the sting off the tongue."

"Similarly, papad is usually served before the main course in most parts of the country, but here in Rajasthan it is served right at the end. It signifies the end of the meal," Ms Kalpana Rai chipped in, enjoying the bewilderment on the faces of our guests. "Why?" asked Gaidik, now smiling and enjoying the conversation along with the delicious food.

"Well," said Rajeev, "I think it is served last because it is said that the dry papad helps to clear the esophagus of any oily remnants of the food and helps in digestion."

I was squirming with spicy discomfort. I wanted to stick out my tongue, aflame with the spicy food, to cool it in the air. I reached out for the tall glass of water kept in front of me. Seeing me, Jean Pierre too reached out for the same and gasped out.

"Why is the food so spicy and oily? Has it got anything to do with the climate of the place?"

Mr Sisodia, who had been quietly enjoying the food as well as our conversation, spoke up, after a long silence.

"Food choices in this state are influenced by the war-like lifestyles of its inhabitants and the availability of ingredients in the desert state. Due to high temperatures, food turns putrid in no time. Hence, food that could last for several days and could be eaten without heating, were chosen to be part of the regular platter. Scarcity of water and fresh green vegetables also influenced food choices. Apart from this, there is an abundance of dried and powdered spices in the state. They are used liberally not only because of ease of procurement but also spicy foods are said to last longer in extremely hot climatic conditions. It is said that scientific experiments have confirmed that consuming spicier foods can help one to beat the heat. It causes one to perspire which cools the body down effectively for a longer period of time."

"Oh wow! I never thought about this!" I said thoughtfully. "It is so different from the food choices in Assam."

My statement piqued everybody's interest. They asked me to elaborate upon it.

"Well, as much as I know," I began hesitatingly, "and as much as I can figure out now, after hearing Mr Sisodia talk about the connection of food choices with the climate and terrain of an area, I can say that even in Assam, the food choices are definitely influenced by the same factors." I continued in a stronger voice as I started getting clarity as I spoke. "Assamese cuisine is very distinctive as it uses spices differently from mainland India. It will be incorrect to say that Assamese food is bland sans any spices. They use spices differently. Assamese cuisine uses a wide variety of rice, fish and greens which are easily available. Apart from this, a wide variety of indigenous foods are available which are rarely found outside this area."

Assamese Cuisine

"Would you be able to tell us something exotic and rustic about the food in Assam? My uncle is a food blogger and I have heard him use these words while discussing Assamese cuisine," said Gauransh.

"I don't know much, but I do remember a telephonic conversation my mother had had with my aunt a few days ago. Assam is a non-vegetarian's delight. Tenga is a common dish of the Assamese which is sour to taste and mostly cooked with fish. Rice, meat and fish are often roasted in bamboo hollows called Bahar Sunga. Vegetarian food is equally interesting. Do you know that banana flowers, which are the buds of the banana plant, are soaked and shredded to use in curries?" I asked, looking around. They shook their heads. Encouraged by the interest reflected in their eyes, I carried on, "We also cook lots of herbs, some of them grow in the wild. Cooking techniques like smoking, fermenting and cooking in banana leaves and bamboo hollows are far from simple and add a distinct aroma and flavour. These techniques have been used since centuries but are quite tricky as people nowadays find it difficult to control the processes of fermentation and smoking in a way that enhances the flavour. It is because of these techniques that the use of spices is minimal."

A Banana Flower

"I would love to see Assamese food being cooked. I thought food can only be cooked on firewood on a wok or a gas stove in some utensil or the other. Using bamboo hollows sounds so exciting!" Gauransh said excitedly and added, "My uncle told me that the Assamese food and style of cooking is very similar to some South East Asian countries like Thailand and Myanmar. It also has a lot of influence from West Bengal."

"Yes, I also remember reading that somewhere," said Ms Rai.

"In Rajasthan, we end traditional food with papad but in Assam we end with raw Tamul (betel nut) and paan," said Gauransh. I nodded my head in agreement.

"I took the liberty of asking my mother to message me some interesting local dishes," I said as I fished out my mobile phone from my sling bag.

"Here are the names of some exotic sounding dishes," I grinned and read on happily, "Khar- it is an integral part of Assamese cuisine. A meal generally starts with khar. The Assamese people cannot do without it and hence the famous saying 'khar khua asomiya'. It is prepared from the banana peel as well as the banana trunk of the banana plant. Next, we also have a severely bitter preparation called Xokota, prepared with dry jute leaf, urad bean and khar. Another exotic preparation is Naroxingho Masor Jul, it's a fish preparation. Pitika is a very popular side dish … the list goes…" I ended with a smile.

Gaidik looked pensive and said, "Dear students, please understand one thing. This is not just a matter of food and taste. It is about respecting and learning from the rich diversity your country has to offer."

We nodded in agreement.

Kalpana Rai ma'am added, "Nationalism and globalization should become platforms to exercise unity in diversity. As the young upcoming generation who is going to take over the reigns of the country, you must ensure that you teach your peers to respect and celebrate this vast diversity in our land. Never allow it to become a matter of silly debate on parochial supremacy."

Lunch ended on a somber note.

Chapter 5.8

ART TALKS - THE RAGAMUFFIN

"Look who is here!"

Hema's voice broke our reviere. We turned around to see and were mystified to see a ragamuffin standing at the doorway between Hema and a tall, thin stranger.

Gaidik's eyes lit up as she realised who stood at The Haveli's doorstep. It took me a moment to realise that the stranger was probably an official from the Jaigarh fort and the ragamuffin was none other than the boy who had returned the purse and was now here at Gaidik's request.

Bholeya

Both Jean Pierre and Gaidik ushered the boy in with gushing tones. The official handed Gaidik her precious belongings and asked her to check the contents. She verified that all was in order and then turned her attention to the boy. Her eyes softened on seeing his bedraggled condition. His hair was dirty and unkempt, clothes were torn and soiled, and eyes were large and sunken in a dull, pinched face. Although he was emaciated, he had an air of quiet dignity around him and his eyes reflected wisdom which belied his age. He introduced himself as Bholeya. He said he lived in a village close to the fort and often went there hoping to get some alms from generous tourists. When asked what prompted him to return the purse as it carried a decent amount of money in Indian Rupees, Bholeya said in a shy voice that his mother had told him that taking something without permission was akin to stealing and that was a big sin, so he returned the purse.

"You never felt tempted to take the money at all?" asked Rajeev incredulously. Bholeya kept looking down at his bare feet and squirmed uncomfortably but refused to answer Rajeev's question.

Gaidik requested Hema to get some food packed for Bholeya and his mother. She and Jean Pierre then tipped Bholeya handsomely. The poor boy's face flushed with embarrassment at the attention which was being showered on him. Finally, with great reluctance albeit with concealed joy, Bholeya accepted the tip. Gaidik quickly scribbled her hotel's address and told him that he could visit her whenever he felt like, till the time she was in Jaipur. Bholeya's eyes lit up happily at this offer as he looked at her with wonder. He couldn't believe the fact that he was being addressed with so much respect and love. We all had a smile on our lips as we saw him scamper away joyfully, duly escorted by the fort official.

That was not the last time we saw him. Little did we know what lay ahead of us.

Chapter 5.9

ART TALKS - MANUSCRIPT PAINTINGS

"Would you like to complete your tour of The Haveli before you leave?" asked Mr Sisodia. We looked at Hema to ask if we had the time as we had to leave for the night safari thereafter. She nodded.

We resumed our tour, totally captivated by the interiors, done up with traditional Rajasthani murals, intimidating yet, interesting display of old swords, rifles and other arms and ammunitions on the walls, impressive pillars, and archways. The mirror inlay work in the main hall of the heritage haveli made us halt there. Our visitors gasped at the sheer beauty and opulence reflected in the hallway.

"We saw this in The City Palace and the Sheesh Mahal too!" Gaidik

Folio from a Kalpasutra Manuscript

exclaimed delightfully.

"Thikri," said Mr Sisodia. "It is a heritage craft of inlaying hand cut pieces of mirrors using diamond scalpels into perfect shapes. These are arranged into frescoes on the ceilings and walls to form geometric mirrored mosaic patterns. This craft is nearly 400 years old."

"Stunning," Gaidik mumbled as she reached out to feel the frescoes. Mr Sisodia led us into a huge hallway which was dimly lit. We could see several long glass cases arranged next to the walls which seemed to have some old manuscripts kept inside.

"What are these?" asked Jean Pierre.

"These are ancient manuscripts from different parts of the country."

"Do you have any such thing from Assam?" I asked excitedly.

"In fact, yes! We do have," replied Mr Sisodia to my delight. He continued his narration, "We have ancient copies of the original manuscripts from Assam. The art of painting flourished in Assam from the 16th century onwards. The Bhakti Movement, which spread in the medieval period through the work of Srimanta Sankaradeva (1449-1569) in this region, helped to give birth to a vigorous culture of literature and art. Srimanta Sankaradeva was also responsible for creation of many literary works and his followers later pursued this tradition. Many scholars elucidate that a significant aspect of the movement was that it recognized the worship of sacred scriptures instead of any formal idol made of stone, wood or any other substance.

The Bhakti Movement led to the development of different branches of art such as painting, drama, songs, dance, and playing of musical instruments. Later years witnessed the proliferation of copying and illustration of manuscripts in countless numbers."

"These paintings have a unique quality," observed Ms Kalpana Rai, "Is this the work of any famous artist whose name is lost in oblivion?"

"No," Mr Sisodia replied, "the craftsmen responsible for creation of paintings and penmanship were known as Khanikars. The Satras, which were the religious and spiritual centers established by Mahapurusha Sankaradeva, patronized and supported them. These Khanikars were traditional carvers primarily associated with woodcrafts and also worked as make-up men during bhaonas which is one of the traditional forms of drama in Assam. Although Khanikars were responsible for creation of beautiful paintings on manuscripts, there is very little information about them. The artists of the Satras mostly believed it to be sacrilegious to inscribe their names in a literary work written by their Guru. These Khanikars were clerics of the Satras who cultivated different art activities along with their regular duties of rendering religious services. Their devotion to the movement led them to render many paintings in a single manuscript. So, it is not possible to attribute this work to any one artist specifically."

"The paper of the manuscript..." Gauransh said, peering curiously at the work, "is the strange colour because of age?"

"Well, yes and no," Mr Sisodia elaborated, "The manuscript leaves or pages as you are calling them, were made of two materials. One was made from Sanchipat—the bark of Saci tree or aloeswood. The preparation entitled a laborious process of curing, seasoning, and polishing the raw slices before the leaves could be made to retain the ink. Second was Tulapat, made of pressed cotton. This was like a handmade paper." Mr Sisodia continued to speak. We were taken aback by what he said next. "It is said that certain manuscripts which carried details of magic and sorcery were made of monitor lizards, deer skins and sometimes used to be wrapped in snake skin," he ended with an impish look.

I shuddered, "I would never touch them!" Everybody had a hearty laugh seeing the horror on my face.

"Are these watercolor paintings?" asked Meera, bending low to see the finer details.

"No," Mr Sisodia said, "Colours were made traditionally by using ingredients like the yellow arsenic to get 'Haital' (yellow colour) and 'Hengul' (vermilion colour). These are most common in the traditional colour palates of manuscript painting. Certain artists today are also trying to recreate and use natural colours by mixing ingredients like xilikha, aamlokhi (amla). These are mixed with cow's urine and kept for about three days. Ou Tenga (elephant apple) seed is added later to make the ink greasy."

"Unbelievable!" exclaimed Jean Pierre.

"What is Xilikha? Sounds so exotic!" asked Priyamvada.

"Xilikha is a type of fruit with a typical flavour called 'keha' in Assamese, which is more close to an astringent taste. This fruit is a major constituent of the popular Ayurvedic medicine called Triphala," Gauransh enlightened us by reading from the internet.

Rajeev interrupted Gauransh in a teasing voice, "I guess you should make your own ink, Genius, and use it in your pen."

Mr Sisodia smiled and said gently, "That is not possible, Rajeev. The ink that is prepared by the traditional method has a very dark colour and it does not run easily unlike modern ink which has acid in it and thus, does not last too long. Since the ink is not refined it does not pass through the nib of modern pens. It can be used only with traditional pens made from bamboo or feathers."

"Gauransh, you just missed your new vocation of being the inkman!" Rajeev said with a loud laugh, much to the annoyance of Gauransh. Meera quickly led Gauransh away before an altercation could start between the two boys.

We thanked Mr Sisodia for enriching our knowledge in the field of art. As we walked back towards our vehicle to move to our next destination, Ms Kalpana Rai summed up the art talk beautifully, "It is very important to study and document the ancient Arts and Crafts today as the traditional knowledge and skill is fast disappearing. If you, as students, do not become actively engaged in the preservation of our heritage, all this knowledge will be lost forever. The first step in this direction is exposure and appreciation, followed by deep study and understanding. It is imperative that your generation works in this direction so that the future generation does not remain bereft of this treasure and also appreciates the contribution of our ancestors in laying the foundation of Modern India."

We agreed with Kalpana ma'am and boarded the vehicle silently.

Chapter 6

TRYST WITH THE WILD - NIGHT SAFARI

Two open Gypsies awaited us to take us around the Jhalana Reserve Forest. It was dusk and we could see the birds flying back to their roosts. There was a chill in the air. We were advised to wear our jackets as it was likely to get very cold in the forest reserve. We divided ourselves into two groups. Each group had its own forest guide. Hema had left us for the day.

She would join us the next day on our way to Ranthambore in Sawai Madhopur.

Our guide was Kanha Ram, an ancient-looking tall, thin gentleman with impressive handlebar moustaches. He started speaking in a sonorous voice, "Jhalana Reserve Forest is spread over an area of 21 sq.km. This picturesque forest is surrounded by the city from all sides. We have had good sightings of the splendid elusive predator, the Leopard," he added knowing it would catch our interest.

We hung on tight. The Gypsy moved silently on the forest trails, traversing the undulating terrain swiftly. The driver knew when to slow down as it would generally be around a favourite haunt of the animals. We pulled our jackets tightly across, put on our hoods and covered our faces with scarves to avoid choking on the flying dust.

"Won't the animals be asleep at this hour? Or getting ready to retire for the night?" Meera asked innocently.

"Oh yes!" Rajeev answered tongue-in-cheek. "Mama leopard would be singing a lullaby for the baby leopard.

But, right now it's dinner time! Meera, how would you fancy becoming the leopard's meal today?" Meera laughed and gave him a playful smack on his shoulders.

Kanha Ram said, "Leopards are nocturnal animals. They venture out at night in search of food. So, if you are lucky, you will be able to spot one tonight."

Prophetic words!

The Gypsy suddenly slowed down and the driver signalled us to maintain silence. And lo and behold! A glorious sight awaited us as we saw a whole family of leopards cross the road. The pack was led by a fully grown leopard, whom we presumed was the mother, followed by three cubs. My heart skipped a beat as the adult leopard paused for a fraction of a second to turn and look at us. I think, for a moment, we all stopped breathing. It was eerie to see the glittery glassy eyes shining in the dim light. "Dinner for the family?" Rajeev murmured. "Thankfully not!" I murmured back as the big cat walked away into the darkness.

As we completed our exciting safari, we came to know that the Jhalana Forest Reserve was home to several animals like the jungle hare, blue bulls, palm civets, hedgehogs and more. It is also a bird watcher's delight as there are lots of Asian Paradise Flycatchers, Indian Eagle Owls, Golden Orioles, Eurasian Sparrowhawks, Nightjars and many more birds that can be spotted here.

"Amongst reptiles, this park abounds with nine different snake

Golden Oriole

species and two species of Monitor lizards," Kanha Ram said as we alighted the Gypsy.

"It is strange to see such a forest reserve so close to the city. In fact it is in a way inside the city itself!" remarked Gaidik. "Don't these animals wander into residential areas?"

"Yes," said Bhuvan Misra sir, "it has happened a couple of times. In fact, each time it has happened, I don't know whom to feel sorry for- the people who get scared witless when they come face to face with these animals or for the poor animal who I think is more scared outside his natural habitat, amongst people who are ready to harm him in the name of self defence."

"Jungles are shrinking," said Ms Rai, "We are getting more and more concrete jungles instead of the natural forest covers. I am glad the government has woken up and is taking active measures to protect our wild friends."

Night Safari at Jhalana Reserve Forest

Chapter 6.1

TRYST WITH THE WILD: INTERLUDE OF DIVINITY – TRINETRA GANESHA

We boarded our vehicle at the crack of dawn. Today, we planned to have a day return-trip to Ranthambore. It was a very cold morning and we moved slowly through an ever thickening sheet of fog around us. It worsened as we moved out of the city and came upon the highway. It was difficult to see anything in the haze. We had embarked upon another exciting journey. As we reached the Ranthambore National Park, Hema said, "Eloping from the grandeur and splendor of palaces and forts, let's now take refuge in the lap of nature."

Jean Pierre remarked, "It's quite intriguing to visit a wildlife sanctuary amidst the precincts of a royal palace, the Ranthambore Fort!"

"Indeed, it can only happen in Rajasthan!" said Debina delightfully.

"What if I told you that the fort has an ancient temple of Lord Ganesha who receives more than 20 kilograms of letters and invitations every day? And that all the letters are read out individually by the priests every day to the Lord without fail?" said Bhuvan Misra sir with a smile.

"I would say that you are joking," replied Gaidik with a smile.

"No, I am not joking," said Bhuvan Misra sir, "this is one of the oldest temples of Lord Ganesh in Rajasthan.

Whenever something auspicious is about to happen, people send the first invitation to this Trinetra Ganesh Temple. Thereafter the priests diligently read out all the invitations. Trinetra Ganesha has two more claims to fame," sir paused and smiled, "the deity of this temple is well known to fulfill your wishes of building a house." Seeing the incredulous looks on our faces, sir continued hurriedly, "Yes, if you happen to walk back from the temple to the entrance of the Fort, you will find lots of flat rock pieces arranged in the form of makeshift shelters, symbolising a house. People are known to send out a silent plea to Lord Ganesha that as I have made a home for you, please get a home made for me too."

"Really!" we all exclaimed.

Sir smiled sheepishly and said, "Yes, even I did it. And out of the blue, I could arrange my finances and get my house built. I attribute it to His blessings."

"This is amazing," our visitors muttered.

"What about the next claim to fame?" asked Meera.

Makeshift Shelters, Symbolising a House

"Well, in the year 1299 CE, during a fierce battle against Alauddin Khilji, King Hammir Singh received blessings from Lord Ganesha in his dream. The war tide turned in Hammir Singh's favour thereafter, and so he built this temple in 1300 CE to appease the God. This is the only temple in the world which has His entire family at one place—Lord Ganesha, his two wives, Riddhi and Siddhi, along with his two sons, Shubh and Labh, and his vehicle, The Musak or mouse."

"Every place here seems to be rich with legends and facts which are beyond comprehension," said Jean Pierre in wonder.

Chapter 6.2

TRYST WITH THE WILD: INTERLUDE OF DIVINITY – THE RED RIVER

We had been cruising smoothly for more than two hours now. We were just about one and a half hours away from Ranthambore. I wanted to tell our visitors whatever I knew about the legend of Kamakhya temple- everything that my grandmother had told me a few years ago. My ancestors had served in the temple hundreds of years ago, so I had a personal connection with it. However, I was a bit sceptical about it as the topic that would come up along with the narrative is somewhat taken to be a taboo, especially if spoken in public...and that too by a girl in front of the opposite sex. I decided to take Ms Kalpana Rai's advice.

The Legendary Red River

"Yes, I am aware of what you are referring to," she said gently in a low tone so others may not hear our conversation. "I think it is high time we broke these old shackles of myopic mentality and learn to speak up boldly yet gracefully. It is nothing but a natural phenomenon so why fear?"

And to ensure that I don't chicken out, Ms Rai made a loud announcement, "Hello everybody! Debina is going to tell all of us about a fascinating legend which will leave you totally enthralled. This phenomenon is tied to an important religious context. Would you like her to speak?"

Everybody clapped and hooted loudly to encourage me. I took a deep breath and began to speak, "Are you aware that Assam has the longest river of India flowing through it?"

"Of course!" scoffed Gauransh. "It is Brahmaputra," he said condescendingly. I smiled as I knew my next question would throw everybody in a tizzy. "But do you know that as per a popular legend the river used to turn red in the month of June for three days every year?"

"But that is as per belief, isn't it? Surely this did not happen in reality?" asked Jean Pierre, totally perplexed.

I hesitated but then decided to be honest, "My great grandmother has seen this to be a fact."

"As per your family legend, Debina?" asked Rajeev cheekily. I felt a wave of irritation engulf me due to his mocking tone. I replied indignantly, "Well, my grandfather also told me that he had seen it happen as a very young boy."

Sensing the tension in the air, Kalpana ma'am intervened, "I am sure there must have been some reason behind it."

"I know," said Gauransh the geek, raising his hand while looking at his tab. I looked at him totally surprised. I had not expected anybody to believe this and thus had broached the topic with a lot of trepidation.

"The first reason is that the soil of that area is rich in iron content. This gives the water a red tint naturally."

I smiled, now ready to enjoy the narration, "But why only for three days, Gauransh?"

He spluttered something incomprehensible.

"Oh, I know," drawled Rajeev, "even I checked online just now. The mountains around the Kamakhya temple have large deposits of Cinnabar or Mercury Sulfide. They have a blood red colour. This bleeds into the river, giving it a red hue."

"Excellent!" I clapped loudly and again asked tongue-in-cheek, "But why only for three days?"

"How would I know why for three days only as per your family legend," Rajeev said, once again in a mocking voice.

I felt my cheeks become red-hot and flushed. I knew Rajeev the rogue was teasing and provoking me and it took tremendous willpower not to fall for his bait. "Not my family legend, Rajeev," I said in a low voice trying to mask my anger, "you can check it up on the internet if you want. These three days the temple doors remain closed for devotees and a huge fair called the Ambubachi Mela takes place in the vicinity of the Kamakhya temple. This fair takes place for three days in the month of June even till the present day. Maybe you would consider attending it next year," I ended up in a caustic tone.

"Cool it guys," Gaidik intervened, "Go easy on each other please."

"Rajeev, the least you can do is to listen to what Debina has to share without getting judgemental and unnecessarily critical about the whole story," Bhuvan Misra sir admonished Rajeev gently.

"Sorry sir! Sorry Debina, I was pulling your leg. Had no intentions of being critical," Rajeev ended with a disarming smile. Mollified by Rajeev's apology I picked up my narration once again.

"Look, the reasons you gave are scientifically valid, there is no doubt about it. But the fact also remains that if it is Cinnabar or the iron content which is responsible for this colour, then it should be for the whole year round, isn't it?" I asked, thoroughly enjoying myself once again.

Kalpana ma'am quickly joined me in this mysterious conversation, "You know some people attribute the red colour to the growth of red algae in the month of June, but even they can't answer why this happened only for three days. Several theories have been propounded but not one of them can answer why the river turned red for only three days."

A strange silence hung in the air as each pondered upon this strange phenomenon.

"Do you know the reason why it turned red for only three days?" asked Gaidik in wonder. Kalpana ma'am looked at me, silently signalling me to speak up.

"Well, no one really knows," I said, "but the answer may lie in an ancient Hindu belief connected to the story of Goddess Kamakhya, around whose temple this strange phenomenon is purported to take place year after year. Would you like to hear the legend?" I asked. They all agreed enthusiastically.

We were not very far from Sawai Madhopur now. I was sure we would reach our destination by the time I finished my narrative.

"A legend within a legend," remarked Gaidik with a smile, "Nothing can get more intriguing than this."

I laughed at her comment and continued my narration, "The legend traces back to the time when Goddess Parvati or Sati as she was called, attended a yajna organised by her father, after her marriage to Lord Shiva against her father's wishes. She insisted on attending the ceremony despite the fact that her father had not extended any invitation to her nor to her husband. Disobeying her husband's wishes, she went to attend the religious ceremony but could not bear the insulting behaviour of her father. Incensed and mortified, she jumped into the holy fire to end her life. Lord Shiva was enraged at the treatment meted out to his wife and got caught in a storm of grief and fury. He slung his wife's body over his shoulder and performed the famous Tandav Nritya or the dance of destruction. It is said that he roamed around the entire universe in an enraged state. Disturbed by this, Lord Vishnu and Lord Brahma tried to intervene but to no avail. In the process, Sati's body got slain into 108 pieces by Lord Vishnu's Chakra. It is believed that each place where Sati's body part fell, is now a Shakti Peeth or in simple words, a point of pilgrimage with very high and intense spiritual vibrations," I paused to let them absorb what I had spoken. Taking a deep breath, I continued, "Kamakhya temple is the place where the Goddess' yoni or womb is supposed to have

Kamakhya Temple

fallen." "But how does this explain the river turning red for three days?" asked Meera "Well, Kamakhya Devi is also called the Bleeding Goddess. It is said that each year the river would turn red every year in the month of June as the Goddess is said to menstruate. Belief in this 'legend' is so strong that even till this day the temple doors are shut for three days to honour this phenomenon of the bygone era. The temple doors are opened on the fourth day for devotees who gather from all over the world to pay their respect to Maa Kamakhya at this time of the year. As I told you earlier, the famous Ambubachi Mela or fair is held during these three days to celebrate this unique event," I ended with a smile.

Silence echoed loudly in the vehicle as the group absorbed this information.

Kalpana ma'am squeezed my hand quietly and patted my head, "I am happy you could speak about menstruation with ease. It is important that everybody understands that this is a natural, biological process and accept it as naturally as one accepts the phenomenon of greying hair." I felt myself glow due to Kalpana madam's support.

"This legend certainly warrants a visit to Assam!" murmured Jean Pierre.

Just at that moment our vehicle came to a halt. We had arrived at Ranthambore.

Chapter 6.3

TRYST WITH THE WILD - RANTHAMBORE

As we once again boarded our Gypsies for our day safari, Gauransh said mysteriously, "Sshhhhhh...hey watch out! The place where you are, can get you a glimpse of the mighty Bengal Tiger even in this broad daylight. So, watch out!"

Hema responded, "You are right. Besides the flagship species of Panthera Tigris or the Bengal Tiger, this place is also famous for Sambar Deer, striped Hyenas, Nilgai, Sloth Bear and a large number of reptiles such as Marsh Crocs, Cobras, Monitor Lizards etc."

The Gypsy had entered the National Park. Dust was swirling in the air. We were advised to pull up our neck scarves to cover our mouth and nose. It was a

Ranthambore National Park

bumpy ride. We were told to keep our voices down and at times to maintain complete silence whenever the vehicle would slow down. At one time, our safari guide asked the driver to slow down. He pointed out pug marks on the muddy trail which was an indication that a tiger may be in the vicinity. Suddenly we saw a flock of birds rise up from a tree and fly away. This was followed by an ear piercing screech from a monkey whom we saw swinging away in alarm from one branch to another till he was no longer visible to us. The driver asked us to maintain total silence. My heartbeats quickened. A tiger was close by. That's why the animals had panicked and the monkey had given out a warning call to the other animals. The predator was here.

More vehicles halted behind us. Word was out. The King of the jungle would soon be in sight. Hema gesticulated frantically to catch our attention as we were looking the other way. I peered at the area she was pointing out. Nothing.

Suddenly, I saw it! It was crouched low in the bushes, silently looking ahead somewhere. His sinewy golden body with black stripes, rippled in the winter sun as he inched forward towards his prey. I held my breath. Hearing the monkey's screech, the pack of blue bulls had disappeared, leaving behind their young calf, who seemed to be struggling to move for some reason. It kept calling out pathetically, probably for his mother, to come to his rescue. What a sight it was to see- a tiger waiting to attack his prey! The prey was in total panic as it had sensed his doom. It was high drama indeed as we saw the pack of blue bulls return, probably to fetch their young one. Rajeev again gesticulated frantically, drawing our attention to a pack of hyenas at the opposite end. Scavengers were waiting to get a share of the hunt. The pack of blue bulls surrounded the calf and we could no longer see it. And then it happened! The mighty tiger leapt out of the bushes, racing to pounce on his prey. There was a huge cloud of dust which blurred our vision. We could just follow the chase for a few seconds. The whole group vanished from our line of vision. We all suddenly realised that we had been holding our breath all along. The palpable tension in the air eased out. Everybody broke into animated chatter. We all had the same thought in our mind, the safety of the blue bulls. Of course, we never got to know what happened. What a close encounter that had been!

"This had my adrenaline pumping crazy!" exclaimed Jean Pierre, eyes still gleaming with excitement of the chase.

We all chorused, "Me too!"

We were now traversing at a very relaxed pace.

Hema began speaking, "I don't think we will have time to visit the Desert National Park close to Jaisalmer, or else you would have been happy to see an excellent example of the desert ecosystem. It is the only place where Rajasthan's State bird, the Great Indian Bustard, the State animal, camel, the State tree Khejri, and the State flower Rohida are found naturally." "Interesting, what about Ranthambore?" asked Gaidik.

Assam State Flowers-Foxtail Orchids

Rohida-State Flower of Rajasthan

"Well, the flora in Ranthambore is mostly a dry deciduous type. Over 300 species of flora have been documented. The most famous trees are Dhok, Dhak, Banyan, Kadam, Jamun, Neem etc." said the safari guide.

"In fact," he continued, "you will soon cross the second largest banyan tree of India. It is so ancient that it is difficult to understand where the actual trunk of the tree is, as it is spread over a large area due to its uncountable number of aerial roots."

We were enjoying the cold, dry wind blowing across our cold faces. Time and again we passed several ruins of the bygone era. It was a unique blend of nature, history, and wildlife.

It was heartening to see several water bodies sprinkled all over the park which must be providing the much-needed relief from the scorching desert heat to the jungle inhabitants.

Guava Vendor in Ranthambore

As we moved out of the National Park, the Safari Guide advised us to purchase guavas to eat, "The guavas of this area are very famous. They are extremely juicy with just the right amount of sweetness." We did as he told us, and believe me, the guavas were one of the best I had ever had!

His next piece of advice to us was to see a unique and interesting natural phenomenon of this region, "You must visit The Great Boundary Fault where the Aravali Plateau meets the Vindhya Hills."

Seeing our confused looks, he elaborated, "The Tiger Reserve is where the Aravali and the Vindhyan hill ranges meet. Perhaps this is one of the contributing factors to the rich biodiversity of this area. Being students and teachers, you will be interested to see that on one hand the geological formations of Vindhyas are characterised by flat table tops while on the other hand, the Aravalis have sharp ridges and conical hilltops."

We were impressed with his geological knowledge and remarked upon it. He blushed like a little child saying, "I wanted to become a professor of Geology, but I am yet to get an opening for the same. So to quench my passion and earn some money, I work as a Safari guide. I am sure I will get to do what I really wish to do, very soon," he ended optimistically.

That was a lesson well learnt by all of us. Never to give up in life. Never stop chasing your dreams. Take a detour if you must, but remain focussed on your destination.

Chapter 6.4

TRYST WITH THE WILD - MANAS & KAZIRANGA

The journey back to Jaipur was full of excited chatter. The thrill of the tiger chase stayed on like a lingering fragrance in a room.

"This place is in stark contrast to Kaziranga and Manas Sanctuaries in Assam, isn't it, Debina?" asked Bhuvan Misra sir.

"Well, of course! The dry deciduous environs of Ranthambore and the wet semi evergreen, tropical moist blanket at Kaziranga and Manas are poles apart," I responded.

Jean Pierre asked, "Have you been to these places in Assam?"

"Yes, I have." I confirmed. "Both these sanctuaries bear the prestigious title of being UNESCO World Heritage Sites."

Kaziranga National Park

"Is it possible to understand why Kaziranga and Manas are UNESCO World Heritage sites?" asked Jean Pierre.

"I have an aunt who is a Systems Ecologist, I am sure she will be able to tell us," said Gauransh.

We looked at him with an amused look. "I guess your family DNA carries the streak of genius," Rajeev mumbled with a smile. All of us suppressed our smiles, for we knew that Gauransh was very sensitive and would not take kindly to his remark.

"What is a Systems Ecologist, for heaven's sake!" Priyamvada exclaimed.

Gaidik replied, "A scientist who studies ecological systems, especially ecosystems is called a Systems Ecologist."

Well, that was something new we learnt amongst so many other things.

Gauransh called his aunt and requested her to connect through a video call for the benefit of his friends, teachers, and visitors. She very graciously consented. We waited for the vehicle to stop midway to freshen up and have some tea and savouries. It was then that we got to meet Sarojini bua, as Gauransh addressed her. "Let's talk about Kaziranga first," she said, adjusting her

Sarojini Bua

spectacles which seem to perpetually slip down her nose after every few minutes. "Kaziranga National Park is located in Golaghat and Nagaon regions of Assam. It is one of the largest tracts of protected land in the sub-Himalayan belt. It has diverse species of all kinds which makes it a biodiversity hotspot."

"The only hotspot I know is the cell phone hotspot I share with my brother at home," whispered Rajeev in my ears. I smacked him hard on his shoulders to shut him up. It would be so rude if we were found to be talking and joking amongst ourselves! Although I must admit that his jokes actually made you splutter with laughter.

Elephant Safari at Kaziranga

"Why has it been accorded the status of World Heritage Site?" Jean Pierre asked. "Well, there are several reasons," Sarojini bua said, once again adjusting her spectacles. She did full justice to the image of scientists I had in my mind- serious, thin, bespectacled with an untidy crop of hair. But she also had pimples!

"A family trait," drawled Rajeev. I looked at him startled as though he had read my mind. He grinned back, shaking his neck in a way which said I-know-what-you-are-thinking. I frowned at him and quickly brought back my attention to what Sarojini bua was speaking about.

Pink Dolphins in the Ganga River

"Kaziranga is regarded as one of the finest wildlife refuges in the world. The park's contribution in saving the Indian one-horned rhinoceros from the brink of extinction at the turn of the 20th century to harbouring the single largest population of this species is a spectacular conservation achievement. The property also provides habitat for a number of globally threatened species including Tigers, Asian Elephants, wild Water Buffalos, Gaurs, Eastern Swamp Deer, Sambar Deer, Hog Deer, capped Langur, Hoolock Gibbon, and Sloth Bear. The park has recorded one of the highest densities of tigers in the country and has been declared a Tiger Reserve since 2007. It provides a safe and healthy habitat to the Ganges River dolphins in some closed ox bow lakes. It is also an important area for migratory birds."

"What is a Gaur?" asked Rajeev, finally paying attention to the conversation.

"It is also known as Indian Bison. It has been listed as vulnerable on the IUCN Red List since 1986."

Sarojini bua shared her screen to show the images of a few animals which fall in the category of threatened species.

"What about Manas Wildlife Sanctuary?" asked Meera.

Gaur Bos

Sarojini bua answered, "Manas is located at the foothills of the Eastern Himalayas. The northern boundary of the park is adjacent to the international border of Bhutan. This place is recognized not only for its rich biodiversity but also for its spectacular scenery and natural landscape. It spans on either side of the majestic Manas River flanked in the east and the west by reserved forests. You will find it interesting to know that Manas is the only landscape in the world where pristine Terai grasslands can be seen merging with the Bhabar grasslands ascending to semi evergreen forests and then to Bhutan Himalayas. The last population of the pygmy hogs can be found in the wilds of Manas and nowhere else in the world."

Sarojini bua continued speaking about Manas, "There is much to speak about Manas but I will tell you only one or two more interesting things. The diverse habitat of Manas is ideal for specialised birds. Manas has the largest population of the endangered Bengal Florican and is a great place to see the Great Hornbill. If you happen to see the website of Manas National Park, you will be able to read a very interesting statement written over there, 'Manas is probably a site of what the Earth looked like before the arrival of man.'"

"Awesome!""Amazing!""Seriously!" Everyone seemed to exclaim at the same time.

"It is also intriguing to see how much pain the government takes to preserve the rich biodiversity of our country. No wonder we are amongst the ten richest biodiversity sites of the world!" said Gauransh.

"But I don't understand, why should we go to such great lengths to protect endangered species?" asked Rajeev. "After all, how do I get impacted if a particular species in a faraway jungle becomes extinct?"

"Good question, child," said Sarojini bua. "All of us are a part of an ecosystem. Studies have shown that extinction of species and unchecked deforestation have a direct impact on human beings. Every species plays its own special role to maintain life on earth. Let me give you an interesting example. Probably, your teachers may recall the incident of 1990's wherein vultures were found to be dropping dead suddenly for no apparent reason. The Indian Vultures which used to number around 40 million birds in the 1990s were reduced to fewer than 100,000 birds, crashing by more than 99.9 percent in some places. Studies revealed the cause of death to be a veterinary medicine called Diclofenac which was routinely given to livestock as an anti-inflammatory drug." We all were hooked to Sarojini bua's narrative.

"But if livestock was being given this drug, why did the vultures die?" I asked.

Sarojini bua replied, "Because the vultures fed on the carcass of dead livestock and consequently died of kidney failure due to overdose of the drug in the livestock's system," she paused, "now, you may wonder how does it matter if vultures die? They are not known for their beauty like peacocks nor for any sweet chirpings like some other birds. But as scavengers they help to keep our ecosystem clean and healthy. Once their numbers dwindled, it had a domino effect which impacted many species and even some cultural beliefs."

"Cultural beliefs?" Gaidik questioned.

"Yes, in India we have a Parsi community who does not bury or cremate their dead. This community depends on vultures to cleanly consume and dispose of the bodies which are kept in specific areas designated for this purpose. These areas are called Tower Of Silence. Without vultures, this community is struggling to find alternative ways of respectfully taking care of their dead."

We listened with disbelief. None of my friends were aware of this, neither was I. "Also, the ecosystem is dependent on vultures to dispose of the carcasses of livestock. Once the vulture population declined, feral dogs and the rat population took over the work of the vultures and in this process diseases like plague, rabies, anthrax became a huge health hazard for human beings." She paused and looked at Rajeev with a smile, "Now you know how you can get affected if the ecosystem gets disturbed? This was a very small example for you."

I let out a deep breath. And so did the others. We thanked Sarojini bua for an enlightening conversation and headed back to Jaipur in silence.

Chapter 7

A NEW ADDITION

The next morning, a surprise awaited us as we reached the hotel of our French guests.

Apart from Gaidik and Jean Pierre who do you think awaited us…it was none other than the ragamuffin Bholeya!

We were surprised to see Bholeya sitting in Gaidik's lap with a tear streaked face and sad eyes. Both Jean Pierre and Gaidik looked very upset.

"What happened?" Kalpana ma'am asked.

"Bholeya's mother is hospitalised for a week or so and his uncle has thrown him out of the house. He has nowhere to go," said Gaidik, looking extremely upset and worried.

Rajeev mumbled, "That's a daily occurrence with these people. They cannot be trusted."

I nudged him to keep quiet.

"What did you say?" asked Jean Pierre, confused.

"Nothing," I stepped in hastily, not wanting Rajeev to sound like a callous person. "He said it is sad that it has happened."

Rajeev looked at me and scowled. "Stop being so judgemental and opinionated, Rajeev," I whispered furiously. Rajeev rolled his eyes up dramatically to dismiss my words.

"I think we can allow Bholeya to travel with us for next few days as he has nowhere to go, if that is alright with you?" Gaidik asked, looking anxiously at our teachers.

Ms Rai and Bhuvan Misra sir looked equally perplexed and didn't know what to say. On one hand, they did not think it to be appropriate for any stranger to join the group and on the other hand,

they felt that their refusal would reflect being very insensitive.

Jean Pierre said hastily, "He is our responsibility and we will take care of him and ensure he does not get into trouble."

So, the matter was reluctantly settled in Bholeya's favour.

It was decided that a few sets of new clothes would be bought for him enroute to Jodhpur and he would also be given a proper bath at our next night halt.

Except for Gauransh, all of us were uneasy about the new addition to our entourage. Something seemed amiss. As we boarded our vehicle, I looked at Bholeya closely. He appeared very nervous and…fearful? I couldn't figure it out. His eyes kept darting left and right and he kept looking out of the window anxiously, as though waiting for someone.

"Forget it," Meera patted me on my shoulder. "Let's enjoy now. I am sure everything will turn out to be fine."

I nodded.

"Jodhpur, Ahoy!" yelled Rajeev to lighten up the environment. We sat back to enjoy the journey.

Chapter 8

OF MINES & MINERALS

Enroute to Jodhpur, Hema announced a change of itinerary.

"There has been a change of plan, folks." said Hema. "We will not stop over at Sambhar Lake but will just view the area in passing."

"What is the Sambhar Lake? Some beautiful tourist attraction?" asked Gaidik.

Hema smiled, "Well, yes and no. Sambhar Salt Lake is India's largest saline lake and is the source of maximum salt production of Rajasthan. Sambhar

Pink Flamingos at the Sambhar Lake

has been recognised as a wetland of international importance. This area is favoured by thousands of pink flamingos and other birds which migrate from Northern Asia and Siberia each year around this time of the year. The specialized algae and bacteria growing in the lake provide striking water colours and support the lake ecology that in turn sustains the migrating waterfowls or water birds," she paused.

"Had we visited that place, you would have seen no water over there as such but you would have been mesmerized by the surreal beauty of white mounds of salt interspersed with dark patches of mud where salt mining isn't taking place."

"But why are we not stopping there?" cried Priyamvada in disappointment.

"You will see when we reach there. Right now, it is sufficient for you to know that the area has been cordoned off."

Moving at a good speed, we were now out of the main city area. Meera had dozed off and so had Bholeya. He lay curled up in his seat, wrapped up securely in Gaidik's shawl. Jodhpur was about three hundred and fifty four kilometers away and we were ready for a long drive of approximately five and a half hours.

"Apart from salt, what else is mined in Rajasthan?" Jean Pierre asked, looking at Gauransh as he knew that is where the answer would come from.

Gauransh perked up and said, "Well, I know that Rajasthan is the sole producer of Lead and Zinc ores, Selenite, and Wollastonite."

He paused, fishing out his tab, "And it is the leading producer of silver, calcite, gypsum, steel and cement grade limestone, feldspar etc. Apart from that it is well known around the world for marble, sandstone, granite etc. You will be surprised to know that 70% of Bone-China tableware is produced in Rajasthan. And it is also ranked second in copper production."

"Wow!" our visitors chorused. "This state is rich in so many different ways!" said Gaidik.

"Well, the list is endless actually." Gauransh confessed. "Rajasthan is very rich in mines and minerals."

"And Assam?" The question was directed towards me. It was Rajeev, smiling. I gave him an irritated look and said, "Why don't you check out the internet and tell us. I don't know anything about this."

He grinned shamelessly and took Gauransh's tab from his hands.

He read through quickly and said, "Let me tell you in a nutshell. Assam is known for its coal, cement grade limestone like Rajasthan, China clay, Iron ore etc. Assam is best known for a mineral called Sillimanite. The Sillimanite deposits in the Khasi hills are world famous for their quantity and purity. It contributes to 90% of total production in India."

"What is this sillimeal mineral used for?" Meera asked, wrinkling her nose in the effort to pronounce the name correctly.

"Sillimanite, silly girl," Rajeev said, correcting her and ducking low as she threw a paper ball in his direction in jest. "Wait, let me check. Well, this mineral is used for manufacturing metals, glass, ceramics, cement etc."

"Hey guys! Guess what, Assam also has gold deposits!" Gauransh said excitedly. "Hello, looking at your excitement, one would think that you will be off to Assam soon for some gold digging!" Rajeev said with a straight face which made everybody laugh.

Gauransh gave a lopsided smile and said, "Maybe." We were pleasantly surprised to see Gauransh take the joke so well. He continued, "Gold is reported to occur in sands, gravels, and alluvial terraces along some of the rivers in the Lakhimpur, Sibsagar, and Darrang districts of Assam. During Pre-British time this important material was collected in many rivers in Assam by people known as Sonowal Kachari."

"Interesting," mumbled a few of us.

Suddenly Rajeev said loudly, "Gauransh, dude, hold your horses for gold digging." "Why," Gauransh asked, " Are you going to join me?"

"No, sir." Rajeev said in the same jovial tone, "Gold-bearing sand used to be panned in ancient times. Now it is no longer an economic proposition."

"Oh!" Gauransh said.

We laughed at his response as it actually seemed that he was disappointed by this piece of information.

"Okay everybody!" called out Hema, "Look out to your left. We are approaching Sambhar Lake."

Chapter 9

THE SAMBHAR LAKE

As the vehicle slowed down we turned to have a look towards our left. What a sight! As far as the eyes could see, there were shimmering mounds and stretches of white sand interspersed with brownish/blackish earth. And we could see movement of some people afar. Gauransh took out his binoculars to have a proper view and then he suddenly shouted, "Birds on the ground! Are they dead? So many of them!"

The vehicle stopped for sometime as we all scrambled to see from his binoculars. Turn by turn we all gasped to see the lifeless bodies of birds, strewn all across. We could see masked men moving about them, probably investigating the cause of death. Hema asked the driver to start moving again.

"This is why we are not stopping at this place," she said in a grim voice. "As per a forest official, nearly 17,000 migratory birds have died so far due to botulism, a serious and fatal illness that affects the nerves. A few days ago on November 10, thousands of birds, including Northern Shoveler, Ruddy Shelduck, Plovers, Avocets, were found dead in the 5-7 km area around Sambhar lake."

We were nonplussed. "What is botulism? Why did these birds die in such large numbers?" asked Kalpana ma'am.

Hema replied, "Botulinum is a natural toxin produced by a bacteria known as Clostridium botulinum. It produces the toxin when it starts reproducing."

"Where is the bacteria usually found?" asked Gauransh.

"It is very common to find it in soil, river, and sea water. Birds get affected by Botulinum C. It affects the nervous system of birds, leading to flaccid paralysis in their legs and wings. In case of waterfowls, this can be catastrophic. In fact, the toxin has been found to be a major cause of mortality in wild birds since the 1900's." "I still don't understand, what happened in Sambhar? How did the birds contract the virus?" Meera asked, confused.

Hema continued patiently.

"Well, let me explain it in this way. This avian tragedy in Sambhar happened due to climate change," said Hema. She paused a while as she saw the bewildered looks on our faces.

Climate change!

Hema continued speaking, "Living organisms like birds, especially waterfowls, fish, and crustaceans such as shrimps, crabs and prawns along with invertebrates like snails as well as planktons like algae, etc are capable of hosting bacteria for a long period of time. The bacteria reproduce through spores and these spores remain dormant for years. They are resistant to temperature changes and drying. Under favourable conditions, the spores get activated. This year we had unusually heavy rainfall. The IVRI report noted that after the heavy showers when the water levels receded, there might have been an increase in salinity levels which could have led to the death of these living organisms. At this point in time, the spores could have been activated."

We were listening carefully. It was difficult to forget the sight we had seen. Hema continued, "So it is believed that the migratory birds fed on these infected organisms which became the cause of their death. It was observed by the scientists in Sambhar area that only insectivorous and omnivorous birds got affected, not the herbivorous." A brief silence followed these words as we absorbed what she spoke. "Environmentalists, ecologists, and other scientists fear that such outbreaks will become a common occurrence as climate change alters wetland conditions to favour bacteria and pathogens."

An impregnable silence followed. We had never realised that the disastrous effects of climate change were now at our doorstep. What had appeared to be distant news headlines was now a stark reality.

Gauransh looked at Hema, "How do you know so much about all this?"

She smiled, "My brother works in this area along with an NGO which is creating awareness about the hazards of illegal salt mining activities that are purported to take place here. And so he knows what is happening. Honestly speaking, I am disappointed we are not visiting Sambar as you would have enjoyed your visit, seeing not only the beauty of the place but also seeing some unique things which you may rarely find elsewhere."

I caught Ms Rai giving a grateful look to Hema for changing the topic as most of us looked visibly shaken by what we had seen and heard.

"Please do tell us about it, Hema," she said quickly.

"Had we stopped there, you would have been taken on a joyride in a petrol locomotive, the only one of its kind in the world. You would have experienced the old world charm in the quaint train."

"Awww!" said Gaidik and Priyamvada together in regret.

"You would have seen a dumb waiter also," Hema said with a smile.

"A dumb waiter?" Rajeev was quick

The Circuit House

to ask, "Would he be dumb as in he cannot speak or dumb as in a nitwit?" he asked cracking a joke, knowing quite well that Hema was referring to something different.

She laughed, "Dumb, as it gives services of a waiter without uttering a word." He widened his eyes, "IT?" He asked loudly.

She fished out a photograph from her bag and showed it to us.

"This is an old circuit house here which is now a hotel. It was the first Circuit House built by the British in India. It is the highest vantage point in the city even today. It gives you an overall beautiful view of the entire area. See, you can see these steps leading up to one of the doors here, which is a washroom. They had kept independent entrance for cleaners to come and clean the washrooms, without having access to the interiors of the Circuit house to minimise contact with the natives. And here , in this photograph , you can see the dumb waiter. It is actually a movable wooden cabinet which is positioned in a lift-like shaft. The cook would serve the food and place it in this cabinet which would be pulled up by the officers. Not only was this convenient, it also minimised contact with the natives."

"Obnoxious!" cried Jean Pierre.

"Yes, the attitude was definitely obnoxious," agreed Hema.

"But the dumb waiter is not obnoxious at all!" said Gauransh excitedly. "I am going to make this arrangement when I build my own house!"

"To avoid whom?" asked Priyamvada with a smile.

"Rajeev," said Gauransh impishly, "he will be the official chef in my house!"

Everybody roared with laughter as

The Dumb Waiter

Rajeev's face turned beetroot red with a scowl.

This time the joke was upon him and he found it hard to take it.

Ms Rai said, "Dear children, let me give you some food for thought. We denounce racial discrimination done by the British. But what about the discrimination that most people do even today in the name of religion, caste, creed, sex, region? It is so subtle that we are not even aware of it most of the time. We have colour and racial discrimination rampant in our society. Look at our obsession for 'fair skin'! One look at matrimonial advertisements or ads of certain 'fairness' products will clearly show you how insecure and disempowered the so-called 'dark tone' people are made to feel!" Ms Rai's face and tone was flushed with indignation. And rightly so! We never really think about these things do we?

"Although," she continued in a milder tone, "fortunately, few matrimonial platforms have declared they will not be mentioning the skin tone now onwards and some products have been forced to change their brand names. But this is not enough to undo the damage done to the psyche of thousands of people. We need to collectively work towards ending this discriminatory attitude amongst us."

Bhuvan sir added, "We even have regional discrimination rampant in our country. People from remote corners of our country are often troubled, heckled, and treated with disrespect as for some reason they are labelled as being anti-Indian. It is painful to see these anomalies in our society. We are fortunate to be a nation with diversity of every kind. But we fall prey to petty politics and instead of celebrating this diversity we end up disrespecting and destroying it. It baffles me why we end up denouncing our own people from remote corners of the country…" his voice trailed off sadly.

Yes, we had got a lot of food for thought.

Chapter 10

THE BLUE SUN CITY - RANBANKA RATHORES

"Welcome to The Sun City of India," said Hema as we entered the city. "I thought you said it was The Blue City!" said Jean Pierre.

Hema smiled, "Yes, indeed it is The Blue City but it is also called The Sun City." "Why?" asked Gaidik.

"Because it remains bright and sunny throughout the year!" said Rajeev.

Hema laughed, "Yes, you are right, Rajeev. Also, the rulers of Jodhpur are descendents of Lord Rama and through him, the lineage traces back to the Sun God (Surya), and so the Rathores also call themselves as Suryavanshi, one from the family of the Sun."

"And why Blue City?" asked Gaidik eagerly.

"There are two reasons which are given for this. I am not sure whether

Ranbanka Rathore

one of them is true or if both hold true. First reason is that it is said that in olden days, a blue colour painted house denoted the residence of a Brahmin family. So all houses that belonged to Brahmins were coloured blue. Which of course does not hold true today.

The Blue City

The second reason is that the colour blue was put over the houses as it has a cooling effect on the structures and would help to mitigate the intense desert heat during summer season."

Our French visitors shook their heads slowly in wonder as each piece of information coming their way was unique in itself.

We arrived at Ranbanka Palace, a heritage hotel, by early evening.

We were excited about staying there as we were told it was amongst the first heritage hotels of the country.

"This is like a dream come true," mumbled Jean Pierre as we sauntered inside the premises. We were struck by the beauty of the place which was replete with intricate marble inlay works, jharokhas, hunting trophies, old fire places, four poster beds and many more old world charms blended perfectly with modern amenities which made it a perfect place to stay.

"The hotel is named after the famous war cry, Ranbanka Rathore, meaning the invincible Rathores," said the porter who showed us to our rooms.

"War cry?" Rajeev asked.

"You want to know more about the war cry?" we heard a voice call out. We turned around to see a gentleman with an aristocratic personality, sitting on an antique armchair, smoking a traditional hukkah. He resembled an old warlord straight out of the pages of some ancient history book. We stopped to hear him speak.

"Ranbanka Rathore comes from a very well known medieval quatrain that describes the different clans of Rajputana. The phrase gained popularity due to its usage on the Rathore Coat of Arms which was designed by Kipling Brothers for the rulers around the first big Durbar in the 1870's. However, the actual Coat Of Arms was finalised at the College of Heralds, London, after approval by the officials of British India. Ranbanka Rathore further became famous as it was adopted by Jodhpur Lancers as their war cry along with the other popular age old war cries like Har Har Mahadev. If you want, you can read the book written by Michael Creese on the Jodhpur Lancers."

"Could you briefly tell us something about the Jodhpur Lancers, sir. I have heard they were known for bravery of the highest order," said Rajeev.

The old gentleman nodded and started speaking with a faraway look in his eyes. "The Jodhpur Lancers were formed in 1889, under the fierce leadership of Sir Pratap Singh. Under his watchful eye, sixty troopers became a path breaking regiment which garnered the admiration of the entire world. In the battle of Haifa, in 1918, they made the greatest cavalry charge ever, on a regimental scale. By the end of the Great War, it is said, no challenge was insurmountable, no order ever refused by and of these extraordinary soldiers who also came to be called as Jo Hukum (as you command)."

The gentleman stopped to take a drag from the hookah.

"What about this hotel, sir? Does it have a history too?"

"Yes, everything in Rajputana has a history. This is the Marwar region, land of chivalry and honour." He paused yet again to take another drag.

"This hotel is owned and operated by direct descendants of the Founders of Jodhpur. In 1927, the current Ranbanka Palace hotel was commissioned as a part of the residence for Maharajadhiraj of Jodhpur, Sir Ajit Singh ji, the youngest son of Maharaja Sir Sardar Singh ji. As Prime Minister of the State, he was allotted this space to make his home. Sir Ajit Singh was known for his fairness and citizens often flocked here, in the main courtyard of Ranbanka Palace, to seek his intervention in key matters." The elderly gentleman stopped speaking all of a sudden as though he wished to sit alone with historical ruminations in his mind.

We thanked him for sharing interesting information with us and moved on to our rooms. I still remember Jean Pierre, shaking his head in wonder and saying, "So much history! And that too when we have just stepped into this city. I am sure our stay in Jodhpur is going to leave us enriched ever more."

We all agreed .

Chapter 10.1

MEHRANGARH FORT

The next day was going to be super action packed. Our first stop was at the world famous Mehrangarh Fort, which is supposed to be one of the biggest forts of India.

Our first glance at the fort intimidated us. Rising more than 400 feet above the surrounding area, it was like a dull burnished crown atop a rocky hill, a mute, majestic testimony to its tumultuous history.

Mehrangarh Fort, Jodhpur

As we entered Mehrangarh, Hema started her commentary about the fort. Her opening statement made us gasp.

"Beneath the foundations of Mehrangarh Fort, lies the grave of a man who died to neutralize a serious curse."

"I am sure you are speaking in jest, Hema," Gaidik said with eyes opened wide.

Hema turned around to look at Gaidik and Jean Pierre who were following her, "No, certainly not. Let me elaborate."

"Rao Jodha, the fifteenth chief of the Rathore clan, is credited to be the founder of Jodhpur. Just as Amber had been the capital of Dhundar area before Jaipur was founded, similarly Mandore had been the capital of Marwar before Jodhpur. A year after his accession to the throne, Rao Jodha felt the need to move his capital to a safer location as the one thousand year old Fort of Mandore was no longer considered to be secured enough. It was decided to build the fort upon a hill known as Bhakurcheeria, the mountain of birds. As per legend, to make the fort, the sole occupant of the hill had to be displaced. He was a hermit called Cheeria Nathji, the Lord of Birds. When requested, he refused to move. Rao Jodha then requested another powerful saint, the female warrior sage, Karni Mata of Deshnok. Seeing a powerful saint in front of him, Cheeria Nathji left the hill but before leaving he cast a curse that Rao Jodha's kingdom would be inflicted by repeated droughts should he build his fort over there. Shocked and dismayed by the curse, the king sought forgiveness from the hermit. Unable to take his words back, the hermit presented a strange solution to neutralise the effect of the curse."

Hema paused to catch a breath. I realised I had been holding my breath, listening to the fascinating legend.

"He said that someone from the kingdom would have to lay down his life by getting wilfully buried alive. When the king failed to find a saviour amongst his subjects, a nobleman called Rajaram Meghwal came forward to sacrifice his life for the greater good of people. And so, Rajaram Meghwal was buried alive on an auspicious day and at an auspicious spot so that the foundation of Mehrangarh could be laid down. It is believed that this happened on 12th May 1459."

"Poor guy!" cried Meera. "What about his family?"

"The king had promised to take care of his family and he did. A sandstone memorial was built over his grave to pay him a tribute. His name, and other relevant details are engraved on the burial stone to acquaint the visitors about all details. If you want, we can visit it."

We certainly did!

The palaces in Mehrangarh fort have been built by several kings over five centuries. We were totally enraptured to see this amazing citadel, which still seems impregnable. We went around the fort in an anti-clockwise direction in a very orderly manner.

Be it the Elephant howdahs or the palanquins used by the nobility,The Daulat Khana which showcased some of the finest and most well preserved collections of fine arts and applied arts, or the armoury which was very impressive and awe inspiring, each area was a living testimony to the grand old past. I was completely floored by the section of Turban Gallery which displayed different types of turbans once prevalent in the then communities, regions, and for different occasions. Rajeev, Gauransh, Bhuvan sir, and Jean Pierre freaked out trying different headgears and getting themselves photographed. Oh, what fun we had!

As we moved out of the fort, Gauransh asked a very pertinent question from Kalpana ma'am.

"Ma'am, we have been hearing about so many legends during this journey. Why are legends important?"

"Very good question, Gauransh. You must first understand what a legend is. A legend is a story about events or actions that have not been proved nor documented in real history.They are retold as though they are real events and are believed to be historical accounts. The details given in a legend are adapted and altered by the community over a period of time, so that they remain interesting for the audience. Legends keep history interesting, because without them there would be no stories. It is often said that legends buffer history else it would appear cruel, unforgiving, and perturbing most of the time."

Bhuvan Misra sir added, "Legends generally refer to a certain period of time with characters who exist in recorded history and a certain geographical reference is also present wherein events are located. In olden days, they kept history alive through the oral tradition in the form of folklores, folk songs etc. No matter how fictitious and romanticised these may seem to be,the truth is, that they are usually based upon facts which are embellished with colourful details over a passage of time. Even the supernatural elements you come across in these legends are meant to be treated as an aspect of truth of a bygone era when such happenings were known to be possible."

We now had more food for thought.

Chapter 10.2

UMAID BHAVAN PALACE & MORE

Our next visit was to the Umaid Bhawan Palace, located on the Chattar hills, with no vegetation around as the hill slopes are rocky. It is one of the largest private residences in the world.

Priyamvada turned towards Ms Rathore and said, "Isn't this the palace that was built to provide employment to the people of Jodhpur after they faced a severe drought with no rains for three consecutive years?"

Ms Rathore replied, "Yes, we can now link the curse that was given by the holy hermit, I guess," She smiled. "The farmers of this area pleaded and sought help from the ruling king at that time, Maharaja Umaid Singh. In response, the Maharaja commenced the work of building this grand Palace to generate employment."

Hema filled in further details, "The foundation was laid in 1929. The construction progressed at a slow pace as the main motive was to provide employment to the famine stricken farmers of the area."

Hema continued, "The Maharaja was a farsighted person. He built a railway line to the site to transport the building material and donkeys were used to haul soil to the top of the site. The sandstone transported by rail was designed at the site into large blocks with interlocking joints so that they could be laid without the use of mortar. The Palace is divided into three sections presently. A part of it is used by the owner, the present Maharaja Gaj Singhji and his family as their residence, the second part is being run by the Taj group as a luxury hotel and the third part is used as a museum."

The dun-colored sandstone structure sprawls over 26 acres of land which includes around 15 acres of beautiful gardens. It is a stunning example of Indo- Saracenic and Neoclassical architecture with Western Art Deco.

The interiors of the palace were breathtakingly beautiful with Makrana marble and Burmese teak interiors.

"Those pants have a very peculiar style," said Jean Pierre, pointing at one of the display items in the museum.

Hema replied, "These are breeches known as Jodhpurs. These are specially designed pants for riders which were first brought into style by Maharaja Sir Pratap Singh of Jodhpur, an avid polo player. He had improved and perfected the initial design from a churidar, and had it first tailored around 1890. It got popular when he visited Queen Victoria in England during her Diamond Jubilee celebrations in 1897. He took his entire polo team dressed in these breeches. The riding gear made a big sensation in fashion circles of the United Kingdom. This was later taken up by the British polo playing community and thus it got famous as Jodhpurs, having originated from this place."

"I believe Jaipur is known as the Mecca of Polo, is it?" asked Jean Pierre. "Indeed!" exclaimed Meera. "My brother is a polo player and this game is extremely popular in Rajasthan, especially in Jaipur and Jodhpur. The Rambagh polo ground in Jaipur, is world famous and witnesses some of the top high handicapped teams slugging it out on the polo field in the month of January each year. Similarly, Jodhpur also hosts high voltage games in the months of November and December."

"What do you mean by high handicapped teams?" asked Gaidik.

"A polo handicap is a system created so teams could be evenly matched when using players with varying abilities. The players are rated on a scale of -2 to 10."

"What is -2?" asked Jean Pierre.

"Minus two indicates a less experienced player, while a player rated at 10 goals has the highest handicap possible. It is very difficult to attain a 10-goal handicap," Meera replied confidently.

"What is the deciding factor for the handicaps?" Rajeev asked curiously to which Meera repiled, "It is the overall rating of a player's horsemanship, team play, knowledge of the game, strategy, horses and of course the skill of the player and his performance in the previous year. My brother told me that there was a time when polo was the only sport in the world that considered sportsmanship while rating a player."

We did not realise that we had been joined by an elderly gentleman who stood listening to our conversation with great interest. We were startled to hear him speak, "Kudos to you, young lady!" he said, addressing Meera. Meera's face turned pink with embarrassment. "I am impressed by your knowledge of this sport. It is called the Game of Kings and the King of Games. You need nerves of steel to play this sport, which happens to be amongst the most dangerous games to be played on earth. And so it is not everybody's cup of tea." He pointed towards the painting of horse polo on the wall and said, "Here you can see one of the greatest games in the history of polo.

Winners of The World Cup Polo Championship in 1957

"In 1957, an official Indian polo team was sent to take part in the World Championship in France that included Polo giants like Major Kishan Singh, Kr Bijay Singh, Rao Raja Hanut Singh, and H.H. Maharaja Sawai Man Singh II of Jaipur. India made a huge impact during the championship, beating all other international polo teams. We lifted the world cup trophy back then. We await to lift it again. This time, we have our hopes pinned on the young and dashing Maharaja Sawai Padmanabh Singh, who is the great grandson of late His Highness Maharaja Sawai Man Singh II of Jaipur. It is a treat to watch him play. We await history to repeat itself."

The gentleman later introduced himself as Thakur Ratan Singh, an old polo enthusiast. I vaguely recalled an Assamese connection to the sport and did a quick check on the internet. Bingo! My memory had served me right. Feeling excited, I shared the Assamese connection with my group members. "Guess what! The game of polo has a

H. H. Maharja Sawai Padmanabh Singh

connection with Assam too! The first polo club in India was established at Silchar, Assam in 1834. It was called the Cachar club."

"Thank you! I did not know this. This information means a lot to me," Thakur Ratan Singh said, patting me on my head. We thanked him for sharing the interesting information and moved on towards the garden area outside the museum.

Gauransh and Rajeev got totally glued to the garden outside the museum where there was a fabulous display of vintage cars belonging to the Maharajas.

It became extremely difficult to pull the two boys away as they couldn't get enough of getting themselves photographed in front of the classic beauties, posing as Maharajas! Even our special guests could not resist the temptation of copying the boys and had a field day posing as royalty, much to our amusement.

We were impressed to know that Jodhpur is strategically located about

Vintage Car at Umaid Bhavan Palace, Jodhpur

250 kilometres away from Pakistan and so it is a key base for the Indian Army, Indian Airforce, and Border Security Force. It was a moment of pride when we were told that Jodhpur's South Western Air Command is one of Asia's largest and one of the most critical and strategic air bases of the Indian Air Force. Salute!

Rest of the day went in a blur as we raced from one spot to another from Kaylana Lake to Jaswant Thada to Rao Jodha Desert Rock Park. This unique park deserves a mention as it is yet another effort to protect the biodiversity of this region. In the face of the climate crisis, all such efforts are laudable.

Chapter 10.3

RAO JODHA DESERT ROCK PARK

Have you heard of the term Baavlia? Well, I had not. It is an invasive thorny shrub introduced from Central America almost a hundred years ago. To think that this variety caused havoc to the natural ecology of a desert terrain thousands of miles away was intriguing to me. Rao Jodha Desert Park had been in a state of neglect

Desert Rock Park

for many years and had been run over by this invasive species, making the place veritably inhospitable for any desert flora to grow there. In 2006, the government took cognizance of the neglect and took up the challenge to eradicate the Baavlia and create a suitable home for native rock-growing plants which belonged to a desert terrain.

The process to eradicate Baavlia was the most challenging aspect. After many failed attempts, the authorities hired Khandwaliya miners to manually chisel around 45 centimetres below into the hard volcanic rock. What a resistant species! The pits vacated by baavlia species were soon used to plant the desert plants which can survive in severe dry, desert heat.

"How do plants survive here?" asked Gaidik.

Our Desert Rock Garden guide was actually a young intern from the University who was doing a course in Botany. He patiently explained some interesting facts to us.

"Plants here can broadly be classified into three categories. First are called succulents. These store water in their tissues, like the cactus and hence, are all effective in overcoming low rainfall."

"Second variety is called Ephemerals. These are by far the most common variety as they live a

State Tree of Rajasthan-Khejri

very short life. The seed germinates when it rains and the plant ceases to exist after the rains get over. These plants evolve not to tolerate drought but to avoid it."

"The third variety is the one which has very long, penetrating roots which can reach deep down inside to draw water from underground. Only a few native trees are adapted to grow in the desert, like the drought resistant Khejri tree."

We have so much to learn from nature. So much to be grateful for. I had heard of plants growing amidst rocks. I had finally seen it. Truly, this desert park is unique in itself.

So different from Assam!

Chapter 11

BHOLEYA

All along, Bholeya had followed us everywhere, holding Gaidik's hand tightly, never uttering a word. As the conversations mostly took place in English language, we wondered if he understood anything at all. Priyamvada and I found it strange that the child kept turning his head to look back over his shoulder, as if searching for someone. The minute he would notice us looking at him, he would hold Gaidik's hand tighter and would shrink back behind her, as though to escape our eyes.

We found his actions very suspicious but could not make out much about it. He

Bholeya

generally managed to be a quiet, invisible member of the group, so we did not pay much attention to him. Though, I must say, it was very heartwarming to see his eyes light up each time he was served something to eat. It equalled the joy he seemed to feel when he got new clothes to wear each day. He would strutter around proudly, preening at himself in the mirror with a silly, happy smile. His usual dull eyes would sparkle with excitement. It was these moments which made us feel happy that this boy was with us. At least he had some cause to celebrate in his otherwise dull, drab, insecure life.

We were now getting ready to travel to Jaisalmer, the Golden City. Jean Pierre had requested me to tell them something more about Assam, the cities, and what they were famous for. He wished to hear of any famous legends from that area as the legends of Rajasthan had left him deeply fascinated.

Chapter 12

KAMARUPA

I had made up my mind to take our guests, my teachers and friends on a remote tour of Assam. As I was not fully equipped to do so, I planned to connect the group with some family members and friends in various parts of Assam. On our way to Jaisalmer, my first video call was made to my maternal uncle, who was a senior Professor at Assam Women's University in Jorhat. I had made a call to him in the morning during breakfast time and requested him to share whatever he could about Assam. And so the call was made and Uncle Parag Bordoloi addressed our group. Gauransh connected us through his tab and very graciously also allowed us to use his bluetooth speakers so everyone could hear Parag Uncle clearly.

"How did Assam get its name?" Gaidik asked. What Uncle Parag had to share with us was extremely interesting. Here is what he said, "There are several theories behind this. In olden days it was not known as Assam but as Pragjyotisha or Pragjyotishpura and as Kamarupa. You may not be aware of the fact that a reference to this State has been made in our two great epics- The Mahabharata and The Ramayana and also in the Puranas with the ancient name of Pragjyotisha. Here Prag means 'former' or 'eastern' and Jyotisha means 'astrology', 'shining'. So it can be said that this was the City of Eastern Astrology."

"Oh! And Kamarupa? Why was it called that?" asked Jean Pierre.

Kamarupa

"Well, the name Kamarupa is associated with an ancient legend," uncle said with a smile.

"I love Indian legends!" cried Jean Pierre. "They are absolutely fascinating!"

"As per the legend written in the Kalika Purana, after Sati, Lord Shiva's wife, immolated herself in the holy fire out of sheer despair of having been insulted by her own father, Lord Shiva was overcome with grief. He began a grim penance and wandered about the world carrying her dead body. His Tandava or the 'dance of death' and the penance alarmed all the Gods because it seemed that this would destroy the world. Debina told me that this part of the story is known to you, so let me tell you what happened after Sati's yoni fell in Kamakhya. Lord Shiva continued his grim penance and the Gods wanted to stop him. It is said that they sent Kamadeva, the God of Love, to make Shiva fall in love again and thereby break his penance. Kamadeva succeeded but Shiva was so enraged by this act that he burnt Kamadeva to ashes with the power of his third eye. It is said that Kamadeva eventually regained his form, Rupa, in Assam and the land where this took place came to be known as Kamrup or Kamarupa."

We were totally enraptured by his narrative.

"But then why is it called Assam now?" asked a puzzled Meera.

"The word Assam is the anglicized version of the word 'Aham' or 'Asom' which was probably given by the Ahom rulers who came to Assam in the year 1228 CE from either Mong Mao, South China or Hukawng Valley, in Myanmar. They ruled Assam for nearly 600 years."

"William Shakespeare had said, 'What's in a name?' If he were alive today and here with us, he would have surely changed his iconic statement and said, It's all in the name!" said Rajeev in an amused voice which evoked laughter amongst all of us. "Indeed!" Gaidik responded with a smile.

Chapter 12.1

JORHAT

We were cruising smoothly on the Jodhpur-Jaisalmer highway. The conversation with Uncle Parag had everybody engrossed.

"Mr Bordoloi," said Gaidik, "If you have the time, could you tell us a little more about some important areas of Assam? I have heard that Jorhat is called the cultural capital of Assam. Is it a fact?"

"Yes, Jorhat is beautiful, a symbol of historical relevance and is truly the soul of Assam. It had been the last capital of the Ahom Kingdom. In 1794, the Ahom king Gaurinath Singha shifted the capital from Sibsagar (erstwhile 'Rangpur') to Jorhat. The place echoes with the bravery of the last of the Ahom warriors who played a key role in liberating the people from the Mughal rulers. Debina can tell you about Lachit Borphukan, the legendary military commander of the kingdom," He paused to look at me. I nodded in agreement and said I would do so later and requested him to continue.

"Jorhat has the world famous Tocklai Experimental Centre. This place is famous for its research work being done to identify the curative effects of green tea and find new varieties of tea. One can also visit the unique 550 acre Mulai forest which came up due to the efforts of one man, Jadav Mulai Payeng, also called the Forest Man of India."

"But what prompted him to develop a forest?" Priyamvada asked curiously.

"I believe the sad plight of a dying snake due to lack of natural cover of vegetation inspired him to do so. He single-handedly worked here to develop this forest cover which now is a home to a large variety of wildlife," said Uncle Parag.

We all simultaneously broke into applause. What a feat!

" You will be happy to know that Shri Jadhav Mulai Payeng has been honoured with Padma Shri, the fourth highest civilian award in India," Uncle Parag concluded with a smile.

We thanked Uncle Parag for his time as he expressed his inability to stay connected any longer.

"The importance of forests cannot be underestimated," said Ms Rai.

"Who will tell me why is it important to conserve forests?" Ms Rai asked, looking at all of us.

"In fact, I think we should let Meera tell us about the importance," she smiled.

Meera nodded her head, paused for a while to arrange her thoughts and spoke, "Forests not only provide habitats for animals and birds but also to a lot of indigenous tribes which would never survive out of their natural environment. Forests are an important source of livelihood for human beings and provide important products and by products like fruits, paper, wood, medicines etc. Forests filter and regulate the flow of water to a large extent due to their leafy canopy which intercepts the fall of heavy rainfall on the forest ground. Thus, the forest floor acts like a sponge and allows the ground to absorb the water. It prevents floods and soil erosion, deposition of sediment in the streams, maintains the habitat of marine life and ensures that the quality of water remains healthy," Meera stopped speaking, indicating she had spoken whatever she knew. Priyamvada spoke up, "One more thing, forests absorb harmful greenhouse gases that lead to climate change."

"I can see your pupils know their lessons very well," Gaidik commented with a smile.

We felt extremely happy to see the proud, beaming smile our teachers directed towards us.

Chapter 12.2

MAJULI

"Uncle Parag did not get the time to tell you about a very important place close to Jorhat- Majuli," I said, "Jorhat has the powerful water body Brahmaputra, which houses the famous island of Majuli. It is the largest river island of the world."

Majuli–Largest River Island of the World

"Really!" the group said in unison. Pleased with their reaction, I started speaking about Majuli, trying my best to recollect everything that I had read about it the previous night.

"Majuli has been the cultural capital of Assamese civilisation since the 16th century. This is as per the written records describing the visit of Srimanta Sankardeva, a 16th century social reformer and polymath, who is revered as the father of Assamese culture. The island has 144 villages in which tribal and non-tribal people live. The locals usually speak Assamese and Mising language and some speak Deori language as well," I rattled on.

"I have never heard of these languages," interrupted Meera.

"Well, actually Misings, Deoris, Sonowal Kacharis are some of the tribes which have been living here since long. Misings form 40% of Majuli's population. In fact, Misings are the largest indigenous community in Northeast India." I ended on a wise note, pleased that I could recall most of what I had read.

"Do you have tribes in Rajasthan as well?" asked Jean Pierre.

"Yes, of course!" exclaimed Bhuvan Misra sir, "the tribes of Rajasthan constitute approximately 13.5% of the State's population. Each tribe, whether it is in Assam or Rajasthan can be identified by their own culture, customs, trades, fairs, and festivals. Bhils and Minas constitute majority of the tribal population of Rajasthan. In fact, the Bhils are one of the largest tribal groups living in Gujarat, Chhattisgarh, Karnataka, Madhya Pradesh, Maharashtra, and Rajasthan."

"Which is the biggest tribal group in India?" asked Gaidik.

"Santhals," quipped Rajeev. We all were surprised that Rajeev had knowledge about this. He was usually the one to crack jokes and speak about sports related topics. All eyes turned towards Rajeev.

"The Santhals are the largest and amongst the oldest tribes of India. They are spread across Bihar, Chhattisgarh, Jharkhand, Orissa, West Bengal and even Assam," he paused and smiled at the mention of Assam. "Since time immemorial, these tribals have cleared forests, tilled the land and have grown food for their own subsistence. They are very good hunters and are well versed with the art of seri culture," he added.

"I have always been fascinated by the tribal way of life and really wish to work closely with them some day," Meera said wistfully.

Gaurang intervened, "Coming back to Majuli islands, guess what! I just read something very interesting about this place." He looked excitedly at us with a gleam in his eye, a typical Gaurang WOW moment.

"Do you know, it is India's first island district and some people say it will dissolve into the river within the next twenty years. It shows up often on lists of disappearing destinations around the world."

We gasped.

"Also," he continued, "It is set to become India's first carbon-neutral district, with the efforts of Majuli Tourism promoting carbon-free travel."

"This is such a dichotomy," sighed Ms Rai. "On one hand, not having exploded in the usual tourist circuit as yet, the unspoiled, intrinsic character of the place adds to its charm and appeal. On the other hand, efforts to bring in tourism to boost the economy are sure to endanger the hitherto pure, rich, unadulterated cultural inheritance."

Gaurang countered, "Ma'am, this place is largely unknown to people even in our own country. Majuli Sustainable Tourism Development Project is working to ensure that tourism here grows at a pace that respects nature and the needs of locals and visitors."

"Well, that is a solace!" smiled Ms Rai.

All of a sudden we heard a burst of music. Rajeev gave a wide grin and said, "Hey! I just found this song on YouTube about Majuli. I think we can enjoy some Assamese rap and learn about this wonderful island."

WELCOME, WELCOME, WELCOME TO MAJULI TO MAJULI,
MAJULI, MAJULI,
IT'S A JEWEL OF THE ASSAMESE
HAIL ALL THE ASSAMESE ASSAMESE ASSAMESE
COME TO OUR SATRAS, TREASURE TROVE OF CULTURAL

ARTEFACTS
ARTEFACTS ARTEFACTS
SEE THE MASK MAKERS IN SAMAGURI SAMAGURI
SAMAGURI
THEY MAKE LOVELY MUKHAS CAN'T YOU SEE COME,
MEET THE POTTERS OF SALMORA THEY MAKE POTS WITHOUT
THE WHEELS
NO WHEELS NO WHEELS NO WHEELS
USING FINGERS AND PALMS AND EVEN FEET FEET FEET FEET
YOU CAN CYCLE HERE AND WALK OVER THERE THIS IS MAJULI,
THE LARGEST RIVER ISLAND MAJULI, MAJULI, MAJULI
BE IT SUNSET AT LOHIT GHAT OR THE YELLOW BRIGHT
MUSTARD FIELDS!
I LOVE TO WALK THE BRIGHT MUSTARD FIELD MUSTARD FIELDS,
MUSTARD FIELDS
NO CARS, NO CARBON, NO CARBON, NO CARS BREATHE THE FRESH
AIR THERE IS NO TAR
WELCOME TO PARADISE MAJULI.

And that's how we spent our time in our vehicle, singing and humming about Majuli. It was super fun as everybody chorused together with full gusto. Before we knew it, we had arrived at Jaisalmer.

Chapter 13

GOLDEN CITY, AHOY!

"We will not be staying in the main city," Hema informed us. "We will be travelling beyond the main city of Jaisalmer to go straight to the Sam Sand Dunes."

A shout of joy went up amongst us. It was a dream come true!

"We will drive past the Sonar Quila, the Golden Fort of Jaisalmer, which is one of the few 'living' forts of the world. It is called living as nearly one fourth of the old city's population still lives within the fort. In other words, for around eight hundred years of its history, the fort itself has been the city of Jaisalmer. It is the second oldest fort of Rajasthan and is also a UNESCO World Heritage Site." Impressive!

Sonar Quila-Jaisalmer

The first look at the fort was even more impressive.

Situated atop a hill, the fort's massive yellow sandstone walls are a tawny-coloured marvel which are known to turn to honey gold colour as the sun sets, providing a perfect camouflage to the fort in the golden coloured sand. The fort stands gloriously amidst the expanse of the Great Thar Desert.

As we drove towards the Sam Sand Dunes, I noticed Bholeya getting restless. Somehow, I was getting more and more uneasy about him. I couldn't forget the time when Priyamvada and I had seen him talking to an ill-dressed stranger. Seeing us approach, the stranger scurried off and Bholeya slinked away. We got no response from him when we asked who he was. But the fear in his eyes stirred the uneasiness in both of us. We decided to keep a close watch on him.

Hema's voice brought me back to her narration of Jaisalmer's history.

"Jaisalmer traces its inception to the 12th century. History tells us that Rawal Jaisal, the eldest son and heir of the Rawal of Deoraj, was passed over for the throne of Lodhurva and a younger half-brother was crowned King. Rawal Jaisal went looking for a new location to set up his capital when he came across Sage Eesul. The sage told him about Lord Krishna's prophecy which said that a descendant of his Yaduvanshi Clan would find a new Kingdom at the same spot. It was in the year 1156 that Rawal Jaisal constructed a mud fort and named it Jaisalmer after himself and declared it his capital."

"Another fascinating legend. It is interesting to note that so many great kingdoms have come up with the blessings of the Divine," murmured Gaidik thoughtfully.

Hema announced cheerfully, "We are very close to our destination, dear friends. Let me brief you about what to expect here. You will enjoy the mesmerizing beauty of Jaisalmer in Sam Sand Dunes. Staying in the tents, perched under starlit sky shall prove to be a once-in-a-lifetime camping experience for you."

"Tent! Will it be comfortable?" Gaidik enquired.

"It will be exciting," Hema smiled, allaying Gaidik's fears.

Sam Sand Dunes

"The spacious tents are fitted with electrical lighting and all other amenities to make your stay comfortable and memorable. Get ready to watch scintillating folk dances and puppet shows , and gear up to treat your taste buds with aromatic and authentic Rajasthani food. Many travellers enjoy the site where sand dunes can be seen as tall as 30 to 60 metres. One may observe the breathtaking views of sunrise and sunset at this place. For the tourists, camel rides are a great source of attraction. Tourists enjoy the jeep drives through the dunes.Parasailing is also one of the major adventure sports practiced here."

"This sounds super fantastic!" Rajeev clapped in glee. All of us followed suit. We were looking forward to one of the best adventures of our life.

Our stay was indeed full of adventure, music, dance, exhilarating camel rides,and parasailing,just as Hema had promised us. Memories of boating in the Gadisar lake, the stunning beauty of the Jain temples, the magnificence of the Patwa ki Haveli will always remain engraved in my heart.

Before leaving Jaisalmer, we learnt something which was unique in itself.

We had Ranchod Bhati, a wizened old man, as our local guide. He had a tall, amiable personality characterised by his colourful turban and unbelievably long, handlebar moustaches along with a frizzy beard. During the course of our conversation, he spoke about the unique water harvesting systems which had existed in Jaisalmer since time immemorial. Water Harvesting is a relatively new term in my personal dictionary. The first time I heard about it was in school when we were told that the school had put up a water harvesting system to collect rainwater in a way that would replenish the underground water level. It was incredible to know that this system has existed in this desert area since centuries! We had seen the fantastic water harvesting systems in the forts and palaces of Jaipur and now we had the opportunity to see the impressive systems in Jaisalmer, albeit out of the Royal precincts.

"We have built these systems because we are staying in a desert area which naturally faces shortage of water due to poor rainfall and intense heat," explained Ranchod Babosa (as he was fondly called by all). "My homeland falls in the arid zone of the country," he said in a hybrid mix of Hindi and Rajasthani language which we kept interpreting for the benefit of our guests. "Although we depend more on animal husbandry than farming, we still need our share of water. We have faced terrible drought-like situations time and again. Rainfall received was between 6 to 7 mm many times, but you will be surprised to know that we still managed to fill the five hundred year old Viprasar pond."

We were intrigued. How was this possible?

What he said next was an eye opener for us. According to him, this pond had layers of Khadia soil and gypsum accumulated on the bed of the pond over millions of years. This prevents fresh water from mixing with the brackish water flowing beneath. Although the surface water is available only for a short time, the trapped water lying below is preserved through beautiful structures called Beri. With the result, water is available to the local people without much problem. This technique is applied to many fields across Jaisalmer. Apart from this, the place abounds in exemplary water architecture in the form of Baoris, Tankas, Joharas, Talabs, Pats, Tobas etc. to name a few."

"Have you ever experienced floods here in Jaisalmer?" asked Jean Pierre curiously.

Ranchod Babosa's face clouded, "Yes, we have." He refused to talk about it further. We sensed the pain of personal loss and refrained from asking more questions. Bhuvan Misra Sir spoke about it before we retired for the night.

"Jaisalmer experienced heavy rainfall about three or four years ago. It was actually unheard of. This

Rainwater Harvesting -Tanka

area is known for its geological feature called 'Hardpan', which does not allow water to percolate below the uppermost topsoil layer. The landscape is not built to absorb or drain away any high volume of water. Climate change is once again responsible for this unprecedented heavy rainfall in this area. As per a study done, many areas are likely to see very intense precipitation which does not necessarily mean heavy rains. It means extremely high rainfall in a short number of days. Erratic, unpredictable weather patterns…" Misra sir's voice trailed off. It was frightening to see the effect of climate change time and again. Till now, it had been a remote event. Here, on this trip, once again, it became a stark reality.

The trip to Jaisalmer ended on a thought provoking note.

Next morning it was time to move to Udaipur with a small stopover at Barmer.

Chapter 14

KIDNAPPED!

The next morning was a nightmare. We were woken up by Jean Pierre's frantic yelling. We rushed out, alarmed by the panic-stricken voice. It took us a moment to calm him down and understand what he was saying as due to intense agitation, he had started speaking in French language, making it impossible to follow what he spoke. He ran towards Gaidik's tent and pointed out that it was empty and both Gaidik and Bholeya were missing.

"Calm down, Jean Pierre," Hema said soothingly, "They may have just gone for a short walk among the dunes. I am sure they will return shortly. I will just send across some people to look out for them."

Bhuvan Misra sir led Jean Pierre to his own tent to calm him down. I looked at Hema. She seemed a bit worried. She told Kalpana ma'am to follow her and asked us to wait. We all felt very nervous as Gaidik had never walked out alone. Feeling restless, we decided to follow Kalpana ma'am and Hema. Seeing us, ma'am told us to come along with her.

"Well, I heard a scuffle behind my tent early in the morning," Hema said. "When I went to check, I could just make out the silhouette of two or three people running away. I did not pay attention," she said with deep regret. "I have informed the authorities about this and they too are looking out for Gaidik."

"Do you think some harm has befallen her ?" Priyamvada asked nervously.

"Let us hope not," Hema said in a grim voice. We could feel our panic rise as each minute passed. All of a sudden, Hema stopped and pointed out a small rock jutting out of the sand.

"Blood!" she gasped out. We stopped cold on our tracks. Lying next to the blood- stained rock was Gaidik's scarf and a single shoe of a child. It was Bholeya's shoe. One of them was hurt! But where were they?

We turned back towards the tent as Hema made frantic calls to some people, giving them the location. She advised Kalpana ma'am to take us back as it no longer seemed safe to be out there and she did not wish to endanger us. Reluctantly, we all turned back and went to update Bhuvan Misra sir and Jean Pierre.

Jean Pierre looked stricken when he heard what we had seen. Pandemonium broke around us, as people went running towards the area where we had been. "What could have happened?" we asked each other in hushed tones. We got further alarmed when we saw Hema's face turn ashen as she spoke on the phone with somebody. She turned around sharply and caught Kalpana madam's arm and took her aside, whispering something in her ears. Kalpana ma'am flopped down on a stool close by in utter

Kidnapped

dismay. We were now very scared. Hema rushed away and we moved towards ma'am swiftly for it seemed as though she may faint in distress. "Ma'am, what's wrong?" asked Rajeev in panic.

"Is Gaidik alright?" "Where is she?"

"Gaidik has been abducted," Kalpana ma'am said in a stricken voice. My blood turned cold. We gasped aloud in horror, "Is she alright?" Meera asked, alarmed.

Ma'am got up and rushed towards Bhuvan Misra sir's tent to find Jean Pierre.

"This whole thing seems like a nightmare," Jean Pierre whispered, burying his face in his hands.

"I wonder what happened?" I asked, feeling numb with fear.

"Could Bholeya be involved?" Priyamvada blurted without thinking. "Bholeya?" said Jean Pierre incredulously, "Why do you say that?"

Rajeev shared whatever we had noticed about him during the past few days. Just as he finished speaking, Hema walked inside the tent, "She has been found," she said with relief evident in her voice. We thanked God and enquired about her well-being.

"She is fine," she said reassuringly.

"But the blood..." asked Jean Pierre with uncertainty. "Most probably it was Bholeya's blood," she said.

"Let us wait for her to come back. She will tell us everything. Meanwhile, please pack up and be ready to leave as we are behind schedule. Gaidik can fill us in with the details as we travel."

It took Gaidik two more hours to return. We all rushed to hug her, relieved to see her back safe and sound. She had taken time to complete all formalities with the local police and a short cursory medical check-up to ensure all was well with her.

Hema ushered us towards our vehicle and we settled down quickly to hear what Gaidik had to say. Bholeya was missing and we wondered if the police had taken him in their custody.

Gaidik began her tale. "I was fast asleep, in the wee hours of the morning. All of a sudden, I heard fierce whisperings around me and felt a scuffle taking place. When I woke up because of the disturbance, I was alarmed to see a tall man inside my tent, manhandling Bholeya. As I opened my mouth to scream, he leapt towards me and clamped his palm across my mouth. Bholeya managed to free himself and run away. I struggled and kicked him viciously to free myself. He suddenly jumped up and ran behind Bholeya. I followed him, not realising what I was doing. I was worried for the poor child and wanted to bring him back. What I saw next, horrified me as I saw the man had captured Bholeya who was desperately trying to free himself. Suddenly, the man took out a dagger to stab Bholeya. I rushed forward and pushed him hard. During this scuffle Bholeya got badly grazed by the knife. The man turned back at me in rage and hit me with something on my head, I fell unconscious."

"Did you get hurt badly?" Meera cried.

"No," Gaidik said, touching her forehead gingerly, "Just a hard knock. There is a slight bump in my head, otherwise I am fine."

She continued, "When I regained consciousness, I found myself tied up on a chair in a dilapidated room. Bholeya was hovering around me, looking worried. I realised he had sprinkled some water on my face to revive me. There was no one else in the room. I signalled Bholeya to untie my hands. He tried but failed."

"Is Bholeya responsible for all this?" Jean Pierre asked anxiously.

"On the contrary, he saved my life," said Gaidik. "He left me after a while and returned with some policemen. They told me what had happened as I had no clue!"

"So, what was this whole drama about?" asked Hema, "I got a call on my cell phone asking for a ransom. We thought you had been abducted to get ransom money."

"Not exactly," Gaidik said. She had started looking tired now, "The police, I believe, had been alerted by the hospitality department of Sam Sand Dunes. They later told me that the man had been Bholeya's uncle who had wanted to nab Bholeya and sell him off to human traffickers. Bholeya's mother had advised him to come to us, so that he could get away from Jaipur for a while. But the wily uncle followed us all through, looking for the moment to nab him. He kept pestering Bholeya to steal money from us and give it to him, but Bholeya refused to do so. Fed up, he came to my tent to steal money and abduct Bholeya. When things went wrong, he imprisoned me and asked for a ransom. But Bholeya led the police straight to me when his uncle went out to make the call. And rest, you all know."

"Good Lord, Gaidik!" we all exclaimed. We were horrified to know about the tough time she had faced.

"But where is Bholeya?" I asked, puzzled.

"Well, the police have him in protective custody. They said they would have him sent back to his mother in Jaipur."

"Poor boy!" Gauransh said, "No wonder he looked petrified all the time!"

Rajeev said, "My uncle runs an NGO which takes care of destitute women and children. The NGO imparts training to empower these women and ensure that the children go to school and learn an employability skill. Ma'am, with your due permission, may I reach out to Bholeya when we return?"

"That is a very noble thought, Rajeev!" Kalpana ma'am said gently, patting him affectionately on his back. Gaidik got up to hug Rajeev and so did Jean Pierre, "You have taken off my worries, Rajeev," said Gaidik gently. "I had been at my wits' end, wondering how I could help the poor boy. I would be grateful if you keep updating me about his welfare."

Rajeev promised to do so.

We were still shaken up by the incident and thanked God that everything had turned out to be well. I sent across a silent apology to Bholeya for mistrusting him. I promised myself that I would never judge people so hastily in life.

Chapter 15

MATKA SAGA

The trip to Barmer was a short one. Most of the time we slept on and off as the morning encounter had left all of us physically, mentally and emotionally tired. Gaidik too got up after a power nap, looking refreshed.

"Everywhere, I see women and girls walking on the road with these earthen pots on their heads. What are these and where are they moving to?" she asked curiously. "These are earthen pots. We call them matkas," said Kalpana ma'am. "These are used by the people to carry

Panihari

potable water from nearby wells or lakes to their homes. Remember, this is a desert. There is always an acute shortage of water here. Water lines have not been laid down in these rural areas. Sometimes, these women have to walk for hours at a stretch to get just one pot of water."

"That is so difficult for us to imagine," said Jean Pierre in wonder.

"But why only earthen pots? These appear highly breakable. Why don't they buy pots made of some metal? Or any other unbreakable material?" Gaidik asked.

"The earthen pots are spherical in shape and made of clay. They act as natural coolants. There are small pores on their surface and water molecules occupy those pores. When warm air passes through them, these tiny water molecules absorb the heat from air and make the water cool," said Gauransh, the fact geek.

"Such a simple looking thing doing something so important!" marvelled Gaidik. "Hey genius! I'm sure you have calculated how much water an average matka holds?" Rajeev's teasing drawl made us snigger.

Gauransh adjusted his spectacles and drew himself up to his full height, holding his chin up disdainfully, "Of course! These matkas are of different sizes and standard matka is of radius 12 inches. It contains 7.238 litres of water."

"Goodness! How do you know it carries 7.238 litres of water for heaven's sake!" Meera said, shocked at Gauransh's prompt reply.

"I always knew you were weak in Mathematics," Gauransh grinned. "Am sure if you knew the formula of calculating the volume of spherical objects, you too would have been able to do that easily."

Meera scowled at him, feeling foolish, whereas all of us had a good laugh. We were happy to see the changes in Gauransh who was slowly improving his interpersonal skills. I saluted Kalpana ma'am's foresight.

Chapter 16

THE WORLD OF ENERGY

A squeal of delight went up amongst us as we saw windmills on either side of the road. The huge, gently whirring giants were things I had only seen in books or documentaries. To see them live in front of my eyes was a treat in itself.

"Behold the Jaisalmer Wind Park. It is India's largest and the fourth largest operational onshore Wind Farm in the world," said Hema.

Jaisalmer Wind Park

That is truly impressive!" said Gaidik.

"What do we get from these windmills?" asked Meera. "They generate electricity," replied Bhuvan Misra sir.

We slowed down to absorb the sight. It was anachronistic. On one hand, we had just left the ancient city of Jaisalmer adorned with beautiful palaces, havelis and forts and here we were in the midst of these sky-rising energy giants which are a symbol of modern age. We slowed down the vehicle as Jean Pierre wished to speak to one of the locals crossing by. He asked the villager what he felt about the windmills and how it impacted his life. Kalpana ma'am did some quick translations for our French guests.

"These windmills are a source of opportunities for our local population as they help them procure employment here. Of course, no technical post is available but small-time jobs as guards etc. come up from time to time. But my nephew who works as a Tourist Guide in Jaisalmer is not happy with these. He calls them modern monstrosities. They spoil the beautiful view from the Jaisalmer fort of stunning sunrise and sunset against the golden sand dunes as these huge giants are visible even from there. I personally do not like them as they create a lot of noise and flickering shadows. Few windmills are placed within 400 metres of the villages where sound levels at times become troublesome. During sandstorms especially, the mills move with such speed and ferocity that the villagers feel these windmills will fall off their hinges. Being a rocky, barren area there is no vegetation to absorb the dull, monotonous drone of these giant machines," said the villager.

We thanked the villager and resumed our journey.

"I just checked online," said Gauransh, "Noise pollution is a serious problem with most people living around the windmills. The noise level of the wind farms have been measured to be well above the threshold of fifty decibels. Sometimes they cross a hundred decibels too."

"It is strange that we have to pay a heavy price in terms of environment, ecology, and pollution to maintain a progressive and comfortable life in the modern era. On one hand, wind is a renewable source of energy and must be tapped as effectively as possible and on the other hand we have this problem affecting people living close by. I wish the government would pass legislation about locating these structures away from the residential areas," reflected Rajeev.

"Who knows, maybe it is already there," said Kalpana madam lightly. "But these issues are manageable, dear ones. Residential areas can be shifted. Everything pales in front of the immense goodness which results from these windmills. Wind energy is a renewable source of energy just as solar energy. It does not contaminate, is inexhaustible and reduces the use of fossil fuels which are largely responsible for the origin of greenhouse gases that cause global warming."

Bhuvan Misra sir added, "And don't forget, wind energy is freely available and this helps to reduce energy imports."

"Thereby creating wealth and local employment," Gaurang pitched in.

"Unlike fossil fuels and nuclear power plants, wind energy has one of the lowest water-consumption footprints, which makes it a key factor for conserving hydrological resources," Jean Pierre enlightened us further.

Rajeev summed up the talk, "Last but not the least, producing electricity through wind energy and its efficient use contributes to sustainable development."

"Yo!" said Priyamvada , giving him a high five.

It was my turn to speak, "As much as I understand, India abounds in both renewable and non-renewable sources of energy-oil and natural gas, solar energy, wind energy, hydel power, thermal power as well as nuclear power. If we talk about Rajasthan, it is rich in both renewable and nonrenewable energy sources. Assam has an abundance of oil and natural gas, hydel power and solar energy too. Am I correct or have I understood incorrectly?" I asked, looking at Kalpana Rai ma'am.

Rajeev spoke before ma'am could answer my question, "Can anyone

Hydro Electric Power Plant-Assam

clarify whether thermal power and nuclear power are the same?"

Silence followed his question which was broken by Gaidik, "As much as I understand Rajeev, in very simple words I would like to say that the main difference between a nuclear power plant and thermal power plant is that in a nuclear power plant, heat developed is used to make steam but in a thermal power plant heat is used to convert steam into electricity," she paused to gather her thoughts and then continued speaking, "Electricity can be generated in different ways, for example, it can be made using solar panels which we have seen in a few places, then it can be made by burning coal or using hydel power. In nuclear power plants, the heat to make steam is created from atoms that split apart—this process is called fission. Uranium is the material used in the fission process."

Bhuvan Misra sir observed, "Rajasthan has rich deposits of Uranium, I guess, that could be one of the reasons to have a nuclear power plant here."

"Quite possible," agreed Kalpana ma'am.

Meera spoke out loudly, "Ma'am!" We were surprised by the tone of her voice, "Could we change the topic, please! It has become too heavy for my liking."

Our teachers laughed watching the expression on her face. But before they could say anything else, Rajeev intervened, "Wait, Meera! Dear teachers, before we are forced to close this rather interesting topic, please tell me which is the safest form of energy to use."

"May I?" Gauransh raised his hand up, volunteering to answer Rajeev's query. What else can you expect from this nerd! As both our teachers asked him to continue, Gauransh started speaking, "All energy sources have some negative effect or other. But the effects vary. Fossil fuels are the worst from the perspective of both human health and climate change. And as we know they are also the main source of greenhouse gases which are actually the primary cause of climate change. Comparatively, modern renewable energy sources are safer and cleaner. It is extremely important for us to stop relying on fossil fuels and gradually transition to nuclear energy and other renewable sources of energy like wind and sun. Personally, I feel this is the only way we can redeem our future." We all gave Gauransh a standing ovation, much to his embarrassment, which in turn left us amused and smiling ear to ear.

Chapter 17

A TRIP TO BARMER OIL FIELDS - BLACK GOLD

We had planned to visit the Barmer Oil Fields. Jean Pierre was highly excited to go to the oil fields. And so were we. None of us had ever visited such a place. Jean Piierre looked at Gauransh and said, "Hey Champ! Tell us what you know about oil fields."

Gauransh was thrilled to be addressed as champ. With great difficulty he controlled the smirk on his face and fished out his tab. Without batting an eyelid he started his documentary on Barmer Oil Fields.

"I would like to begin by quoting, 'Never give up because great things take time'. This quote absolutely fits in the story of Barmer Oil Fields. In 1998, Royal Dutch Shell Company, one of the biggest names in the field of oil and natural gas, started their exploration for oil with a 100-million dollars investment. The bore-well which they drilled came up dry and the logging tool- a probe sent down into the well to get electrical readings, produced a printout that strongly suggested absence of oil.

But Cairn Energy Plc., a relatively little-known Scottish company with a 10% stake in Shell's Rajasthan leasehold, had a technician at the site who claimed to have noticed oil dripping off the probe when Shell pulled it out of the well. So Cairn

Barmer Oil Refinery

paid the full cost of the next drill in exchange for a 50% stake in Shell's Rajasthan property and found a tiny sink well of oil. In 2002, Shell sold Cairn its remaining 50% stake in the unspectacular Rajasthan property for $7.25 million." We listened with rapt attention as Gauransh rattled off- partly reading, partly narrating.

"After many unsuccessful attempts and sinking around $100 million into the Rajasthan desert, the Cairn team had almost lost all hope of finding oil there. They made one last attempt and a miracle happened. Just a mile north of Shell's original well, they found one of the largest stores of oil. On getting this huge success William Gammell, Cairn's Chief Executive stated- It's always wrong to quit halfway through your drilling program. That was the story of how the Barmer oil fields were discovered," ended Gauransh with a flourish. "I never knew the story of an oil field could ever be interesting," said Priyamvada dryly.

"Any oil fields in Assam?" asked Gaidik, looking at me.

I nodded my head vigorously and took Kalpana madam's permission to connect with Biswajeet Gogoi, our close family friend and a retired engineer of Digboi Oil Refinery. She acquiesced.

Biswajeet Baba, as I used to call him, agreed to have a talk with us reluctantly. I suspect he was a bit nervous facing foreigners and a bunch of naughty children.

"Assam is known the world over for the Digboi Oil Fields which are one of the oldest oil fields, located in the town of Digboi in the Tinsukia district of Assam," he continued. "You will be amused to know that the town got its name from the phrase 'dig-boy-dig', which is what the British used to tell the labourers as they dug for crude oil."

This brought a smile to every body's face.

Digboi Oil Refinery

"Dig-Boy-Dig," whispered naughty Rajeev in my ears, "becomes Digboi! Oh boy!" he sniggered.

I gave him a hard nudge again to keep quiet and signalled him to listen respectfully. He grinned apologetically and started paying attention to what Biswajeet Baba had to say.

"The discovery of oil took place in an unusual way in Digboi. A popular legend says that more than a hundred years ago, a band of intrepid pioneers who were searching for the black gold, accidently happened to notice that the elephants who had been put to work for laying of a railway line, had oil stains on their legs when they walked out of the nearby dense forest carrying logs of wood.

The men began exploring more and after a few years the British started a small oil installation. This way Assam Oil Company was formed in 1899 to look after the running of

The Oily Clue

the oil business in this area. India, as well as Asia obtained its first refinery in Digboi in the year 1901," Biswajeet Baba ended with a small smile.

"Is there any difference between an oil field and an oil refinery?" asked Meera. "Yes," Baba said, "An oil field is the place from where crude oil and natural gas is produced. An oil refinery is an industrial plant where this crude oil and petroleum is refined. There are more than one hundred oil and gas fields in Assam but only four oil refineries- Noonmati refinery, Numaligarh refinery, Bongaigaon refinery and Digboi refinery. Out of these, Bongaigaon, is the largest oil refinery."

"I must confess, we never really focus on the difference between oil fields and oil refineries! It is crystal clear now, thank you!" said Rajeev sincerely.

"How many oil fields do we have in Rajasthan?" asked Meera.

"Well, if I recall correctly, Rajasthan has approximately sixteen separate oil and gas fields of which the major reserves are located in the area in and around Barmer. Even the oil refinery is located in Barmer. Apart from this, there are reserves to be found in Gujarat also. Assam, Rajasthan, and Gujarat are the three largest producers of mineral oil or crude oil in India," said Biswajeet Baba.

We had gotten very late and so the visit to the Oil refinery had to be given a miss. We just drove past the area and decided to proceed straight to Udaipur. Meanwhile, Gauransh had a few questions to ask from Biswajeet Baba.

"With so many oil fields in India, I am sure India produces enough oil to take care of its needs? Are we exporting oil also?"

"On the contrary, son," Biswajeet Baba replied, "India is one of the largest importers of oil in the world. It imports nearly eighty percent of its total oil needs."

"Oh!" we exclaimed as that was news to us.

"But why are we producing less oil?" asked Gauransh puzzled. "Are our needs more or is less oil being produced?"

"Good question," said Baba, impressed by Gauransh's persistence. "Experts are of the opinion that most of our country's crude oil production comes from aging wells which have become less productive over a period of time. A lack of new oil discoveries coupled with a long lead time to begin production (because of red tapism) has led to steady decline in India's crude oil production. This has driven up our need to import domestic crude oil. We import nearly 80% of our total need."

"Is that why we get affected by the international rise and fall of prices?" asked Priyamvada thoughtfully.

"Good inference drawn, kiddo!" exclaimed Biswajeet Baba. "A fall in price would drive down the value of its imports. This helps narrow India's current account deficit."

"What does that mean?" asked Rajeev.

"It refers to the amount India owes to the world in foreign currency. A fall in oil priced by ten dollars per barrel helps reduce the current account deficit by $9.2 billion, according to a report by Livemint."

"And an increase would result in just the opposite…" Meera's voice trailed thoughtfully.

"Yes, that is correct," said Biswajeet Baba.

"How long will our crude oil reserves last?" I asked anxiously. "If crude oil reserves dry up we will be in very deep trouble, won't we?"

Baba smiled, "Don't get so anxious, Debina. Technically, the world over, the possibility of crude oil reserves getting completely exhausted is very remote. Yet, the fact remains that what remains underground after some time tends to be of poorer quality. Most of it is termed as 'heavy' or 'sour'. As you are aware, oil and other fossil fuels are finite resources by their very nature, but as easier reservoirs of oil get exhausted, other more complicated reservoirs become economically viable. Deeper reservoirs and other more technically challenging ones are usually more expensive to exploit. But as long as there is demand for oil, they will get extracted for use. Although you must also know an important fact- as per some reports available as of 2018, we have around 50 years of crude oil and gas left at current consumption levels."

We gasped, "Fifty years down the line, we all would still be alive and living! How will we survive?" Rajeev remarked in dismay. Although his remark made us laugh, yet, undoubtedly it was a worrying thought.

"It brings us back to the observation made by Gauransh near the windmills. We need to focus on transition to alternate sources of energy," said Priyamvada thoughtfully. "We seem to depend on oil and fossil fuels for literally everything in our life," she continued, "be it food, clothes, computers, pharmaceuticals etc., they all depend directly or indirectly on crude oil and other fossil fuels either for production or transportation. Loss of these resources would have a profound and crippling effect upon the world."

Meera continued Priyamvada's train of thought, "I guess innovation is needed in the area of replacing nonrenewable sources of energy to renewable sources of energy for production, usage and transportation of goods. Research and development is required in shifting the base from oil and fossil fuels to renewable sources of energy like wind, hydel power, geothermal power, solar energy, rain, tides etc."

"Otherwise get ready for doomsday," said Gauransh in an ominous tone.

On this disturbing note, we bid farewell to Biswajeet Baba and proceeded with our journey. We were now on our way to Udaipur.

Chapter 18

THE STORY OF INDIAN CHAI

Udaipur was three hundred and thirty-three kilometres away. We were now scheduled to reach Udaipur very late at night. Our journey was interspersed with lots of talks and short power naps which we took turn-by-turn.

"Most cities of Rajasthan seem to have sobriquets, am sure Udaipur also has one," Jean Pierre enquired.

"Udaipur does not have only one rather it has three sobriquets," Hema responded smiling. "It is popularly called as The City of Lakes, it is also called as The White City, and is also referred to as Venice of the East."

"Interesting, it sounds like a very beautiful place," Gaidik said. She looked at me and asked whether Assam cities too had sobriquets.

"Yes, they do! And very interesting ones at that!" I replied. "The city of Guwahati is called the Gateway of North East India. If you have Venice in Rajasthan, we have a Switzerland in Assam," I said lightly, "Haflong is called the Switzerland of the East. Tezpur, another city in Assam is called The City of Blood."

"City of Blood!" Gaidik exclaimed in horror. "Why?" she asked .

"It is connected to an ancient legend," I replied. "The legend is of Banasura, the great Asura king of the ancient city of Tezpur. He had a beautiful daughter, Usha. Usha's best friend's name was Chitralekha who was a mystical artist with magical powers. As per the legend, Usha saw a handsome prince in her dreams and fell in love with him. She described him to her friend Chitralekha who painted a portrait of the Prince as per the description.

On completion of the portrait, Chitralekha recognised him to be Aniruddha, ruler of Dwarka and grandson of Lord Krishna. Chitralekha spirited Aniruddha away to Usha's chamber where they got married as per Gandharva rites. When Banasura discovered their clandestine relationship, he imprisoned Aniruddha which led to the arrival of Lord Krishna to rescue his grandson. A huge, bloody battle ensued and the entire city was drenched in human blood, hence Tezpur came to be known as the City of Blood."

Chitralekha's Portrait of Aniruddha

"Fascinating!" said Gaidik and Jean Pierre simultaneously.

"Even Brahmaputra has a sobriquet. It is called Sorrow of Assam- most probably because of the frequent floods in this river and the large-scale destruction that the floods cause," I added.

"I think you also have a place called The Tea City of India?" Gaidik asked hesitatingly.

"Dibrugarh!" said Priyamvada triumphantly and looked at me for confirmation. I nodded my head, "Correct, my dear!" I said affectionately.

"Let's get a taste of Assam till we reach Udaipur," Jean Pierre said. "So, Debina, will you tell us or connect us with some expert who will tell us more about the Assam Tea?"

I smiled, "Both I guess. I will tell you little of what I know and the rest can be told to us by my cousin Bijoy who works in the tea gardens."

"Perfect!" our guests said in unison.

"India's original tea city, Dibrugarh is located on the banks of the river Dibru and it is the largest tea producer of the country. This place is a perfect blend of natural beauty, tradition, and culture. History of Assam tea is around two hundred years old when the British decided to plant their own tea from China. They then discovered a wild plant growing here in the hills which had a tremendous potential of sourcing good quality tea. Assam's tropical climate provides a perfect environment for tea production. They explored the potential and rest as they say is history," I smiled while simultaneously trying to connect with my cousin through a video call. He finally picked up.

Bijoy bro gave me his usual toothy grin and happily shared whatever he could with us.

"Could you tell us a little bit about tea farming?" asked Jean Pierre after the customary greetings.

"Tea comes from the tea plant Camellia sinensis, which grows best at high altitudes. More than five years are required for the tea shrub to start producing leaves that can be commercialized, and the plant can stay productive for over 100 years. In general, tea can be harvested all year round, but there are peak seasons when high quality tea is plucked.Assam tea is generally harvested twice, in a

Camellia sinensis

'first flush' and a 'second flush'. The first flush is picked during late March. The second flush, harvested later, is the more prized 'tippy tea', named thus for the gold tips that appear on the leaves. This second flush, tippy tea is sweeter and more full-bodied and is generally considered superior to the first flush tea. The leaves of the Assam tea bush are dark green and glossy and fairly wide compared to those of the Chinese tea plant. The bush produces delicate white blooms. Once plucked, tea leaves are delivered within a few hours to an estate processing factory often situated within the compound of a tea garden. Processing of tea has to be done immediately after plucking in order to retain quality. After processing, 'made tea' is sent either for direct selling or to a warehouse for auction. An average of half of total production is sold through auction. There are a total of nine auction centres in India. In auction, tea is bought by buyers who then market it after blending and packaging. On average, it takes 20 to 30 weeks for tea to reach consumers."

"Riveting journey I must say," remarked Kalpana ma'am. We all agreed.

"Does tea production have any effect on the Indian economy?" asked Jean Pierre, remembering the import saga of crude oil.

"You bet it does!" exclaimed Bijoy bro, "According to estimates, the tea industry is India's second largest employer. It employs over 3.5 million people across some 1,686 estates and 157,504 small holdings, most of the workers being women. In Assam and West Bengal, the two main tea growing regions of India, tea plantation workers are mostly Adivasis or tribals who are descendants of workers forcefully recruited and brought by colonial planters more than 150 years ago from neighbouring states such as Jharkhand, Bengal, Bihar, Odisha, and

Tea Garden, Assam

Madhya Pradesh to work exclusively on the plantations." He paused for a while to recall some more facts and continued, "India is the second largest tea producer in the world. First being China. It was ranked fourth in terms of tea exports a few years ago. At the same time, India is also the world's largest consumer of black tea, with a domestic market consumption of approximately 911 million kg of tea as per the last figures I know of. Tea production is headed by Assam in India followed by West Bengal then Tamil Nadu and also Kerala." Bijoy bro paused and suddenly exclaimed, "Hey! I can't see you guys!" It was then that we realised that darkness had descended all around us.

"Yes, we are travelling, so I guess you cannot see us as there are no lights here," I said.

I looked at Gaidik and asked her if she wished to ask anything more. She nodded, "Bijoy, what you told us is absolutely wonderful to know. We would like to know more about some other aspects. Would you have the time to talk to us?" "Sure ma'am," Bijoy bro said, his teeth gleaming as usual.

"Actually, roaming around in Rajasthan is a unique experience. Could you tell us about any unique place in Assam which is known to very few people?" asked Gaidik.

"There are many places. I will tell you about a couple of them. First is the Umswai Valley in the Karbi Anglong Plateau area. I went there last year with my friends. The place is largely undiscovered due to lack of accessibility. This place is worth a visit because of many reasons. You would be awestruck by the natural beauty of this place with wild flowers growing out of nowhere and also by the ethereal mist which covers the hills of the Karbi Anglong Plateau throughout the year. This place is inhabited by the Tiwas tribe also known as the Lalung tribe. The life of the Tiwas tribal people makes for an interesting study. This indigenous tribe is found both in Assam, Manipur and Meghalaya. The Tiwas tribe is further divided into two sub- tribes depending on where they live. One sub tribe is called Hill Tiwas as they live on the hills and the other is called Plain Tiwas as they live in the plains near the southern bank of Brahmaputra valley. Interestingly, both the groups have different cultures and speak different languages. The Hill Tiwas have an ambilineal descent. In most cases, the husband goes to live

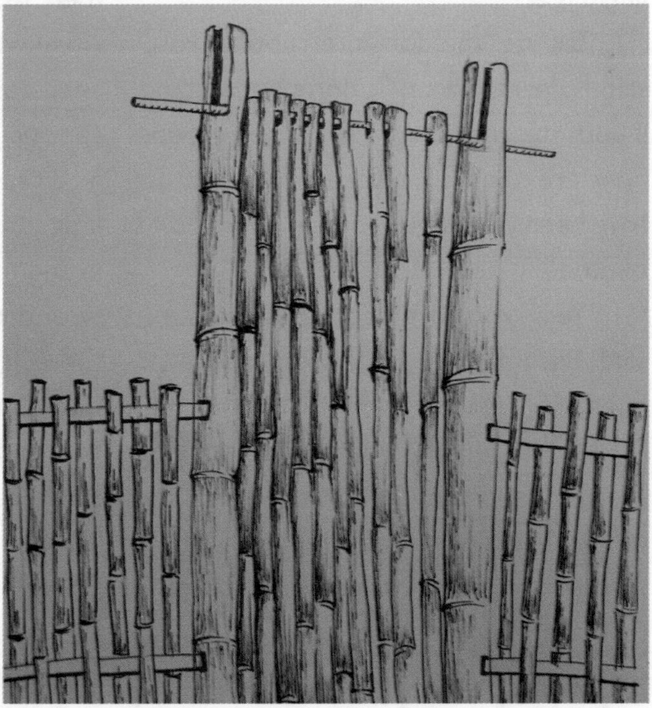

Wind Chime Bamboo Gates in Umswai Valley

with the wife's family after marriage, and their children are included in their mother's clan, whereas the Plain Tiwas people have a definite patrilineal descent. Nowadays, the trend is changing under the influence of neighbouring tribes which are mostly patrilineal. Even the language spoken by both the tribes are different. On one hand, the Hill Tiwas people speak the Tibeto-Burman language of the Bodo-Garo group, on the other hand the Plain Tiwas people speak Assamese language."

"Excuse me for interrupting you," said Kalpana ma'am. "I don't understand, if both the groups are Tiwas tribe groups, how are they so different? They must have been one large group at some point of time?"

"Yes, you are correct, madam," said Bijoy bro. "I had asked a similar question when I had visited the Hill Tiwas. As per the local people living there, the Plain Tiwas did not like the inheritance of the matrilineal system and certain sacrificial customs that were practised in the group. So they moved out of the hills to live in the plains."

"Interesting to know about the societal set up. I am amazed at the diverse cultures and beliefs that so enrich your country," said Gaidik softly.

"That is why we call it Incredible India," I said with obvious pride.

"True, Debina," Bijoy bro nodded his head in agreement. "Let me share another interesting belief of the Hill Tiwas people. They perform a prayer ritual known as Phidri Chongkong at a village named Amsai Pinu. This is performed every year by a handful of men from the tribe. As a part of the ritual which is performed to honour the ancestors, they erect a monolith in a specific area of the village. This ensures a disease free and prosperous Tiwa kingdom. This ritual is done once a year in the month of March. There are about two thousand monoliths to be found there. It is an unusual sight in itself."

"One monolith each year, two thousands of them in one place," muttered Gauransh thoughtfully. "Does this mean that the Tiwas tribe has existed in this place for about 2000 years?" We were startled by his calculation and looked at Bijoy bro with questioning

Stone Monoliths at Umswai Valley, Assam

eyes. He smiled and nodded his head, "Seems like it, young man."

"What an ancient tribe!" exclaimed Jean Pierre.

We started losing our internet connectivity with Bijoy bro so we quickly thanked him for his time and ended the call.

Udaipur was still a few hours away.

Chapter 19

HAIL MEWAR!

"Welcome to the land of Mewar. To a land of unmatched courage and bravery," said Hema as we approached Udaipur.

"You have been to the Dhundhar region in and around Jaipur. You have been to the Marwar region, in and around Jodhpur. Now you will see a part of the Mewar region, in and around Udaipur," she said.

Her tone drove the last vestiges of sleep and tiredness away from our eyes.

"Another city with royal lineage?" asked Jean Pierre.

"Yes, a glorious royal lineage," she said with pride, "It is the place where the Maharana is not the King of Mewar but a mere custodian."

"Custodian? Custodian of what?" asked a puzzled Gaidik.

"The royals of Mewar have never considered themselves as kings. Despite their title of Maharana, the Mewar royals consider themselves custodians of Mewar, ruling their territory only on behalf of their family's presiding deity, Shree Eklingji. The deity is called the king of Mewar. Mewar was initially known as Medhpaat and its head of State Lord Shiva, as Medhpateshwar. Over the ages, the name Medhpaat became Mewar. As Lord Shiva was believed to be the ruler, they called themselves as Maharanas and not Rajas or Maharajas."

"Unique!" mumbled Gaidik. We all thought the same.

Shree Eklingnath ji, Eklingji, Custodianship Unbroken Since 734 CE

"Which areas come under the region of Mewar?" asked Bhuvan Misra sir curiously.

"Mewar includes the present day districts of Bhilwara, Chittorgarh, Pratapgarh, Rajsamand, Udaipur, Pirawa Tehsil of Jhalawar district, Neemuch and some parts of Madhya Pradesh and Gujarat," said Hema.

We had heard about a few places she had mentioned but many names were new to us. "That sounds like a huge area!" said Kalpana ma'am.

Hema smiled. She seemed to be an ardent fan of Mewar as her commentary on Mewar was laced with pride and passion. I can never forget the conversation we had that night, nor can I forget Hema's fervent face and tone.

"This is the land that evokes memories of valour, honour, and glory. The legendary figures of Mewar make this place the epitome of defiance and custodianship of their heritage, even at the cost of their lives. Defiance was a jewel adorned not only by the men but even the women of this region. This is the land of the beautiful Rani Padmini who defied the evil intentions of Allaudin Khilji by preferring to immolate herself in the holy fire of Jauhar, rather than surrendering to the enemy. This is the land of Panna Dhai who sacrificed her own son to save the future king of Mewar. This is the land of Meera Bai who defied all customs, traditions, and conventions for her steadfast and unequalled devotion to Lord Krishna. The land of Hadi Rani who sent across her chopped head as a memento to her husband so he would not get distracted by her presence during war time. The land of Rana Kumbha, a giant of a personality, who fought tirelessly to keep invaders at bay. This is the land of Rana Sanga whose valour did not abate even upon losing an eye and an arm. He proved to be one of the toughest opponents of the Mughal Sultanate. Mewar shall ever sing the glories of Jaimal and Patta, who died in the defense of Chittorgarh, fighting till their last breath against the invading armies of Akbar. And Mewar will forever remain indebted to Gora and Badal who also valiantly put their life at stake to save the honour of Chittorgarh. The saga of the legendary heroes of Mewar would be incomplete without speaking about Maharana Pratap, one of the greatest heroes of Indian History." Hema paused to catch a breath. We were so taken up by her animated and passionate talk that we didn't realise when we disembarked from the vehicle and checked into the hotel. Dinner was a haze as we hung on the riveting account of Maharana Pratap by Hema.

"Maharana Pratap was the thirteenth king of Mewar. According to Satish Chandra, who is a historian,

Rana Pratap's defiance of the mighty Mughal Empire, unaided by other Rajput states, constitutes a glorious saga of Rajput valour and self-sacrifice for cherished principles. Maharana Pratap is held in very high esteem for never compromising on his ideals even in the worst of adversities."

"Who was the founder of this great Mewar dynasty?" asked Gaidik.

"Bappa Rawal," Hema answered. "As per the ancient text of Eklinga Mahatmya, he founded the Mewar kingdom in the year 728 CE. He is the one who built the temple of Eklingji, dedicated to Lord Shiva."

"So which places of Mewar are you going to show us, dear Hema?" asked Gaidik.

"We will first visit Kumbhalgarh, then Chittorhgarh. Last will be the city of Udaipur," Hema told us.

We were very excited and looked forward to our exciting trip around Mewar.

Chapter 19.1

KUMBHALGARH

We reached Kumbhalgarh by mid-morning.

"Early history of this fort is obscure. Kumbhalgarh in its present form was developed by none other than Maharana Kumbha. Kumbhalgarh is one of the most spectacular forts of India. It has the second longest wall in the world after The Great Wall of China," said Hema.

"Wow! That's news to us, isn't it?" said Priyamvada looking at Meera and me. We nodded enthusiastically. Hema continued, "This Great Wall extends thirty six kilometres over the horizon hugging rich forests and embracing over three hundred and sixty temples and palaces inside the fort precincts."

"The fort must be huge!" exclaimed Jean Pierre.

"Yes, Kumbhalgarh is one of the largest fort complexes in the world and the second largest fort of India after Chittor. It is also a UNESCO World Heritage Site," said Hema.

The vehicle came to a halt indicating that we had reached our destination. As we got out, we were greeted by a blast of cold wind which made us reel on our heels. It was a cold, hazy morning. The sun was hidden somewhere behind the mist and the clouds. As we walked upto the fort we were struck by the stony grandeur which stood a mute testimony to its glorious historical past.

Hema began her commentary, "The fort stands tall at an elevation of 1100 metres and is perfectly perched between eleven peaks of the Aravalli ranges. Its strategic position

Kumbalgarh

atop a high ridge camouflaged by the surrounding peaks has made it as one of the most important and probably the only impregnable fort of the state."

When we looked up at the vast expanse of the fort, the sturdy rounded bastions drew our admiration even before we entered the mighty Kumbhalgarh fort. "There are seven imposing gates called Pols guarding all possible entries to the Kumbhalgarh fort. You can hear the whispers of history as you walk the magnificent ramparts of the fort, purportedly wide enough for eight horses to march abreast," said Hema as we walked through the first Pol or gate. "Impressive," said Jean Pierre.

As we walked along the somber corridors of the ancient fort built in the fifteenth century, we felt as though we belonged to a long forgotten era. We felt intimidated by the sheer size of it.

Hema continued, "Kumbhalgarh also separated Mewar and Marwar from each other and was used as a place of refuge for the rulers of Mewar during times of danger. A notable instance was in the case of Prince Udai, the infant king of Mewar who was smuggled here in 1535, when Chittor was under siege. Prince Udai later succeeded to the throne. The fort has remained veritably impregnable to direct assault."

We stopped for a while in silence at the place where Rana Pratap had taken birth. It was called Jhalia ka Malia near Pagda Pol. I saluted the great warrior who had fought tirelessly to live up to his ideals and to free Chittor. His fiery never-say-die spirit is a source of inspiration to one and all.

"As an ode to this great personality, let me narrate a touching story from Maharana Pratap's life to you," said Hema softly.

"Maharana Pratap had a dream to avenge the annexation of Chittor. After the fierce battle of Haldighati ,Maharana Pratap redesigned his strategy of tackling the Mughals. He moved his capital to Kumbhalgarh, his place of birth and commanded his subjects to leave for the Aravali mountains and leave behind nothing for the approaching enemy as the war would be fought in a mountain terrain which the Mewar army was used to but not the Mughals. It is a testament to the young king's respect amongst his subjects that they obeyed him and left for the mountains. The Bhils of the Aravallis gave him full unstinted support as they held him in very high esteem. Maharana Pratap used his guerrilla war tactics very effectively to time and again inflict damage upon the Mughal camp. Maharana Pratap took harsh measures to remind himself, and all his subjects, why they were undertaking this pain-to win back their freedom, their right to exist as they wished. He swore that he would eat from leaf-plates, would sleep on the floor and would not shave till the time Chittor was liberated. In his self-inflicted state of penury, the Maharana lived in huts made from mud and bamboo. In one incident that caused him extreme pain, his children's meal (bread made from grass) was stolen by a dog.

"It is said that this cut deeply into Maharana Pratap's heart. He began to have doubts about his resolute refusal to submit to the Mughals. Perhaps in one of those moments of self-doubt, Maharana Pratap wrote to Akbar demanding 'a mitigation of his hardship'. Overjoyed at this indication of his valiant foe's submission, Akbar commanded public rejoicing, and showed the letter to a literate Rajput

Maharana Pratap- The Roti Episode

at his court, Prince Prithiraj who was the younger brother of Rai Singh, the ruler of Bikaner, a State established some eighty years earlier by the Rathores of Marwar. He had been compelled to serve Akbar because of his kingdom's submission to the Mughals. An award-winning poet, Prithiraj was also a gallant warrior and a longtime admirer of the brave Maharana Pratap. He was astonished and grieved by Maharana Pratap's decision, and told Akbar the note received by the Mughal emperor was a forgery done by some foe to defame the Mewar king. He requested and obtained Akbar's permission to send a letter to Pratap, ostensibly to ascertain the fact of his submission, but in reality with a view to prevent it. He composed and sent across a few couplets that exhorted Maharana Pratap to never give up his steadfast campaign against the might of the Mughal rulers. Upon reading Prithiraj's heartfelt entreaty, Maharana Pratap once again picked up his fallen spirits and continued his crusade till his last breath. Unfortunately, he could never liberate Chittor but he lived by his oath of sleeping on the floor and eating on leaf plates till the very end."

A silence enveloped us as soon as Hema ended her account. We all felt transported back into the times of Maharana Pratap and felt truly moved by the deep conviction, constancy of aim and effort, and total dedication of this great Rajput king.

Kalpana ma'am reflected, "An indomitable spirit leads to courage and deep faith in one's cause keeps one going strong even in face of the worst adversity," she paused, "when the cause is just, it does not die with its protagonist. It lives on till it is achieved. In this case, freedom for Chittor was the aim. The pursuit never died with Maharana Pratap. It lived on till it was achieved by his grandson, Hammir."

As usual Kalpana ma'am had given us food for thought. Inner strength is the key to resilience.

Chapter 19.2

CHITTORGARH

Chittor was a little less than four hours away from Kumbhalgarh. The sun was finally out and shining and we were looking forward to our visit to the largest fort of India. A fort which has witnessed events that have fired the imagination of poets, authors, lyricists, artists, and movie makers alike.

"Hema, please tell us something about Chittorgarh fort," said Kalpana ma'am. Hema nodded her head absent mindedly and began speaking.

"Fiercely independent, the fort of Chittor was under siege three times in its history. Each siege was fought with unmatched valour and bravery which gave rise to numerous tales of courage, pride, and romance that the bards of Rajasthan have been singing for centuries. This fort has also witnessed three Jauhars."

"What is a Jauhar? I have heard you mention this word earlier too," said Jean Pierre.

"Jauhar was committed by the Rajput women when the outcome of a battle went against the Rajputs and defeat was deemed to be imminent. At that time, all the women living in the fort would dress up in their wedding finery and along with their children would prepare to immolate themselves in the holy fire amongst Vedic chants being recited by the royal priests." Our French guests had incredulous looks on their faces. "They burnt themselves alive willingly?" asked Gaidik, horrified.

Jauhar Kund

"Yes, they had no other way of saving their honour from the enemies," replied Hema.

"What about the men?" asked Jean Pierre. "The men committed Saka," said Hema.

This intrigued us. We knew about Jauhar but Saka was new to all of us.

"The night after Jauhar, the men would don kesariya and apply ash on their foreheads from the fire of immolation of their women and children, put a Tulsi leaf in their mouth and ride out to fight the enemy till death. Rajput men and women preferred death to being captured alive by the enemy, especially if it were an enemy from a foreign land," Hema ended on a sad note. We were shaken to the core to know this.

"Tell us more about the three Jauhars you spoke of," Bhuvan Misra sir said. "We are aware of Rani Padmini's Jauhar, but didn't know about the others."

"Well," began Hema, "as you rightly said, the first Jauhar took place in 1303 CE when Ala-ud-din Khilji besieged the fort of Chittor under Rana Rawal Ratan Singh. Rani Padmini

Vijay Stambh, Chhitorgarh

along with the entire entourage of women in the fort of Chittor, committed Jauhar and went down in the annals of history. The second Jauhar was committed by Rani Karnawati, wife of Maharana Sanga. Maharana Sanga died after the Battle of Khanua in 1528 CE, thereafter, Mewar and Chittor came under the regency of his widow, Rani Karnawati. Besieged by Bahadur Shah of Gujarat, Rani Karnawati along with all the ladies of the fort committed Jauhar in 1535 CE while the men committed Saka the next day. As per a popular legend, during the siege of Bahadur Shah, Rani Karnawati, sent out a Raksha Sutra to Humayun, the Mughal King, imploring him to help a sister in distress. Humayun, apparently was touched by the entreaty and went out to help her but arrived too late. This, as per the legend, marks the commencement of the festival of Raksha Bandhan in India, whereby a sister ties a Raksha Sutra on her brother's wrist after which the brother pledges to protect his sister all his life."

Hema paused. "Oh wow! Is that true?" asked Gaidik .

Hema shrugged, "It is a popular legend. There are no historical accounts to check its veracity."

Hema continued, "The third Jauhar took place when Akbar besieged the fort of Chittor in September 1567. The royal family was taken away for safety through secret passages. A fierce battle ensued wherein Jaimal Rathore and Patta Sisodiya put up a huge resistance to the mighty Mughal forces. When all seemed lost despite a bitter resistance put up by the Rajputs, the women committed Jauhar in February 1568. Even Akbar could not help acknowledging the sheer bravery and valour that was displayed by Jaimal and Patta. Till date one can see two cenotaphs built between the second and third gate of the fort, which were built to honour the memory of these two heroes of Mewar," Hema concluded.

We hung on to each and every word spoken by her. It was so interesting to know about little known facts of history, although, as Kalpana ma'am told us in private, she was not sure how authentic these accounts were.

Disaster struck!

A traffic jam made us come to a grinding halt. After waiting for a long time, we were told that the road to Chittorgarh was blocked as an accident had taken place. Clearance would not be possible for the next four hours. Much to our disappointment, it was decided to take a detour back to our hotel in Udaipur.

"Unbelievable!" cried Rajeev in disappointment and we followed suit, equally dismayed by the turn of events.

Kalpana ma'am tried to pacify, "An important life skill for you to master is that it is not possible for things to manifest as per your choice or as per your plan every time. Key to success lies in your ability to accept the change and adapt accordingly."

Well! Easier said than done! However, we knew ma'am spoke the truth and understood that most people suffered in life because of non-acceptance of change and rigid behaviour. Those who become slaves to their plans often end up miserable in life.

So! Accept. Move on.

We adopted this mantra and decided to make the best of the journey by listening to Hema and seeing her presentation on…you guessed it… Gauransh's tab!

Let me recall and share the synopsis of Hema's presentation.

"Here is a picture of the magnificent Chittorgarh Fort which is located upon a seven-mile-long hill, covering 700 acres of land with its fortifications, temples, towers, and palaces. The earliest history of this fort is difficult to trace, but it's believed that Bhim, the legendary figure of the Mahabharata, visited this place to learn the secrets of immortality and became the disciple of a sage, but his impatience to perform all the rites deprived him of his goal, and out of sheer anger he stamped on the ground creating a water reservoir, this reservoir is called as Bhimtal."

She continued, "There are many places worth visiting inside the fort precincts. You can see monuments which commemorate either a victory or stand as a mute testimony of some important historical event. As mentioned earlier, this place has an indelible impression of some of the greatest legendary figures of all time, who will always be remembered in the annals of history with deep reverence."

A View of Chittorgarh Fort

Hema looked at us questioningly and asked,"Who can recall a few names for me?"

We started reciting the names turn-by-turn,I quickly said, " Rani Padmini." "Maharana Sanga, Maharana Pratap," said Priyamvada.

"Rani Karnawati," said Gauransh. "Meera Bai," Rajeev pitched in.

"I have heard of Meera Bai," Gaidik interrupted, "Wasn't she a devotee of Lord Krishna?"

"Yes," Hema said softly,"one of the greatest devotees of Lord Krishna. She epitomises faith and surrender in God's name."

Hema's face took upon a dreamy look as she spoke of Meera Bai.

"She withstood severe ridicule and persecution at the hands of her family for her unwavering love for Lord Krishna. In her beautiful poems she has alluded to two attempts on her life. On one occasion it is said that a poisonous snake was sent to her in a basket of flowers, but when she opened it, she found an image of Lord Krishna. She has also composed another poem which states that she was given a cup of poison which she drank fearlessly yet suffered no harm. It is said that towards the end, her physical body merged with the statue of her beloved Lord Krishna and she disappeared forever. Such was the devotion of this great mystic saint."

Hema stopped speaking and seemed to be lost in her own reverie. We too felt the need for silence and quietly sat in our seats, absorbing what we had been told.

"What a sharp contrast she was from the fierce scions of Mewar," observed Jean Pierre.

Indeed!

Hema quickly altered everybody's mood by saying something completely different.

"Chittorgarh fort is also called the Water Fort."

"Water Fort?" asked Meera and Priyamvada simultaneously.

"I thought this fort would only be known for its bloody battles, stories of matchless courage, fiery spirits, and irrepressible pride," said Rajeev drily.

"Yes," Hema smiled, "primarily for the reasons stated by you. Well summed up, Rajeev! But let's not forget, this too is a desert region with shortage of water. You saw the brilliant water

Meera Bai

management at Nahargarh, Jaigarh, and Amer in Jaipur. You also saw the unique system in Jaisalmer. Now, let us see the water management system of Chittorgarh fort."

Hema zoomed the picture to a water body inside the fort and continued, "The fort had 84 water bodies, out of which only about 22 exist today. These include ponds, wells, and baories-stepwells. All the ponds have a natural catchment. The wells and stepwells are located below the ponds, so that even the seepage from the latter is not lost."

She paused to search for a particular website and thereafter clicked on Chittorgarh.com. She read out some interesting information from the site for us. "The fort spreads over 700 hectares, 40 percent of which are given over to water bodies. The average reservoir depth is about 2 metres. Taken together, this means these reservoirs can store about 4 billion litres of water," she paused as she saw me getting restless. The figures were not making sense to me. I couldn't relate with them. I told her so. She signalled me to wait and read further, "This means that in a year of good rainfall, enough water would be stored to last the next twelve months. Even after water loss due to seepage and evaporation and other causes, an army of 50,000 soldiers could live in the fort for four years without fear of thirst."

"Wow!" we all exclaimed.

"Now, that's quite impressive!" said Gaidik.

"Now you know why this place is so special?" asked Hema.

"Yes," said Jean Pierre, "The history of this fort is a unique amalgamation of devotion, dedication, and determination."

"We will come back next time to actually see the fort in person. It is a strong incentive for us to return soon," added Gaidik.

We clapped with glee upon hearing these words.

Chapter 19.3

CRAFT CLUSTERS

Enroute to Jaipur, chatting merrily amongst ourselves, we did not realise that the speed of our vehicle had slowed down considerably. We looked out of the window and were pleasantly surprised to see a colourful melee of rural men, women, children, and huge camels with highly embellished camel saddles weaving their way through a roadside bazaar which is called a Haat.

"How much water does a camel's hump hold? I have heard about it but don't know much," said Jean Pierre.

"None. That is a fallacy," Gauransh elaborated. "A camel's hump does not hold water at all. It actually stores around eighty pounds of fat which is used by the camel for nourishment when there is scarcity of food. Once the camel has used the fat inside its hump, the hump turns limp and droops down. With proper rest and food, the hump gets restored to its original size."

"How do these camels survive in the desert heat?" I asked.

At that moment I realised I had always been fascinated by camels but had never really had the opportunity to talk about them.

Gauransh the geek enlightened the group, "A camel's physiology enables it to survive the harsh desert environment. Camels have bushy eyebrows and two rows of long eyelashes that protect their eyes from the sun and the severe sandstorms. Similarly, they have the ability to close their nostrils to keep the sand at bay.

Large, tough lips enable them to pick at thorny, dry vegetation without getting hurt and their big, thick footpads help them to walk amidst the shifting desert sands and rough, rocky terrains."

"That's one of the finest examples of adaptation I have heard," Kalpana ma'am complimented Gauransh. His face broke into a big smile and he continued, "Does anybody know how much water a camel consumes at a go?" We shook our heads.

"Camels rarely sweat, even if the temperatures go extremely high, they are not known to sweat easily. So whatever fluids they consume they are able to conserve it for a long time. When they drink water, they tend to soak up water like a sponge. A very thirsty camel can drink around thirty gallons of water in only thirteen minutes!"

We were amazed by this piece of information.

"And so this hardy desert animal is called The Ship of The Desert," Gauransh ended with a flourish.

The vehicle was now literally crawling through a crowd of shoppers. Gaidik and Jean Pierre were particularly enamoured by the colourful bedsheets of patchwork and mirror work on display at various places, the bangle stalls shimmered with glass and lacquered bangles as they glinted scintillatingly in the sunlight. Tiny mementos made of lac also seemed to be a major draw for the shoppers. The Rajasthani footwear, jootis, were another sight to behold as were the blue pottery wares on display.

The tie and dye printed fabrics along with block printed ones tempted all of us to stop and purchase some things. We were advised not to do so as the area was crowded. We also saw beautiful puppets for sale. We were delighted to find articles with intricate gem paintings and exquisite pieces of miniature paintings on silken fabrics. Tribal jewellery in silver attracted most of us. Our French guests were very amused to see metal cow bells and highly colourful braided tassels which are bought by proud camel owners to embellish their Camelus friends. As the crowd started thinning out, we came across a lone vendor selling handmade paper products. Hema said it was safe to get down and have a look.

Jean Pierre and Gaidik were

Blue Pottery with Block Printing

enchanted by the feel and look of handmade paper. Gaidik couldn't help marvelling at the beauty of the handmade sheets embossed with rose petals, gold thread and blades of green grass. She caressed the sheets softly and asked us to share what we knew about this special paper.

"First of all, I am curious to know what this paper is made of," said Gaidik.

Meera volunteered information this time. Her uncle was in a partnership with a handmade paper export firm and she had a fairly good idea about this product. "Handmade paper primarily consists of raw material like waste paper and hosiery cloth. To obtain the texture grass, silk waste and flowers are added to the main ingredients. Most of the time flowers which turn waste after being used for wedding decorations are used," she paused, "let me share whatever little I know about the history of handmade paper briefly with you. Handmade paper crafts go back as far as the 16th century. The Mughals brought it to India from

Turkey. The early paper artisans made special paper for the Mughal court. This craft was patronised by Maharaja Sawai Ishwari Singhji of the Jaipur Royal family. In Rajasthan, Sanganer in Jaipur became the main center for making handmade paper as this place had water and open spaces. During olden days most craftsmen belonged to the Kagzi community. The term Kagzi is derived from the term Kagaz, which means paper."

"Interesting," Gaidik mumbled.

Rajeev pitched in with an equally interesting piece of information, "Handmade sheets are also made by using waste cloth, paper and—believe it or not—elephant dung!"

"Are you joking?" asked Priyamvada warily.

"No, he is not," Meera said with a smile, "The use of dung began in Jaipur some time back and is an excellent way to upscale a waste product, in this case, elephant dung."

I recalled something and further added, "Even in Assam, the same thing started a few years ago. Inspired by the use of elephant dung for making paper, a gentleman from Assam experimented using rhino and elephant dung to make natural paper."

Gauransh took the conversation to the next level by adding, "Yes, they mix elephant and rhino dung with waste paper as most of the grasses these animals eat are not fully digested and constitute a large part of their waste. It is an excellent method employed by some small scale entrepreneurs who have very innovatively chosen the ecological route to preservation and waste management."

Rajeev, never to be left behind in the information sharing race said, "In Assam, they create products with dung paper, bamboo, and banana stalk strips and other such natural materials found locally over there. Narrow bamboo strips are cut with a simple knife and are then inserted into the paper to form a textured surface for a product. When inserted into paper, bamboo strips form a designed surface."

"My mother has several bamboo textured sarees too!" I said excitedly.

Jean Pierre smiled, "From rose petals, grass, and silk fabrics to bamboo strips, elephant dung and rhino dung...what an amazing amalgamation of unlikely features to form this unique product." We agreed.

Kalpana ma'am said, "You will be amused to know that cow dung is not only a source of manure and cheap fuel in India but is now being seriously explored to make items like eco-friendly bricks and even paints. Most modern paints, used to paint our homes, are notorious for being the biggest culprits of spreading in-house pollution and toxicity. So the natural paints made from cow dung will be eco-friendly."

"Unbelievable," said our guests, shaking their heads in wonder.

Our guests purchased some handmade paper letter pads, envelopes, bags, and small containers as gifts for family and friends back home in France and then we resumed our journey back to Udaipur.

"Debina," Kalpana ma'am addressed me, "You just mentioned that your mother has sarees made from bamboo fabrics, what about silk? I have heard that Assam is famous for its silk too, isn't it?"

"Yes ma'am," I replied, happy to answer her query as I had a fair idea about this topic.

"The cultivation and weaving of wild silk is rooted in the life and culture of the people of North East India, especially in the state of Assam. Assam is well known for different types of silk but I would like to tell you about the rather unknown Eri silk. It is very different from normal silk as unlike regular silk, this one is processed without killing the silkworm. I am sure you are aware that normally silk cocoons are boiled

Life Cycle of Silk Moth (Eri Silk)

with the worm inside to maintain one continuous filament, which results in a smooth and shiny fabric. Interestingly, the Eri silkworm spins short segments of a filament and creates a cocoon that is open at one end enabling the moth to emerge. This peace silk is, therefore, a very popular fibre among vegans and Buddhists. Eri silk is funnily enough also known as the silk of the poor. The status of eri clothes in the folklife of Assam is reflected in an old Assamese proverb 'Dair pani, erir kani', which implies that while curd (yoghurt) cools, eri cloth warms up a person. Nevertheless, this Eri silk has excellent qualities—it is very strong, combining the elegance of silk with the comfort of cotton and warmth of wool. And above all, it is completely non-violent," I ended, happy to see the rapt attention everyone paid to my talk.

"I never knew all this!" cried Meera and Priyamvada simultaneously. "I will always try and get Eri silk products

Weaving of Eri Silk

now," said Priyamvada seriously, "I never realised that the smooth, satiny feel of silk that we all enjoy, comes at the cost of violence caused to innumerable silk worms!"

That was a sombre thought indeed. Unknowingly, we become a part of violence directly or indirectly and we never pause to reflect upon the choices we make in our life for the sake of convenience. More care needs to be exercised if we wish to maintain a balance on planet Earth.

Bhuvan Misra sir spoke after a long silence, "I recall that during the early period in Assam history, bamboo had a lot of religious significance and it was forbidden to be cut on certain days which were considered to be auspicious."

"Yes sir," I said, endorsing sir's views.

"Bamboo is found in great abundance in Assam and is still revered by many people. However, cane and bamboo products of Assam are now famous all over the country and there is a huge demand for it.

Bamboo Craft, Assam

Mekhla Chadar with Collage of Meenakari Work, Lac Work, Mojari, Moga Silk, Bandhani

The famous headgear of the Assamese- the Japi- is also made using bamboo amongst other things. This traditional headgear lends a very distinct identity to the people of Assam just as the Rajasthani headgear called safaa or paag lends a distinct identity to the people of Rajasthan."

"Well said, Debina!" exclaimed our French guests, "Thank you for summing it up well for us."

I beamed happily.

Udaipur was close by and gradually we all dozed off quietly to combat the wave of tiredness that engulfed us after the day-long journey.

Chapter 19.4

THE CITY OF LAKES - UDAIPUR

Udaipur was the last halt of our trip. I could sense the regret amongst all of us...regret that the tour would soon come to an end. But as the saying goes, everything that has a beginning has an end too. We were determined to make the last leg of our journey, a memorable one.

As we drove towards the Udaipur City Palace, Hema enlightened us about the history of the City of Lakes.

"The Mewar dynasty is deemed to be one of the oldest dynasties of the world. Udaipur was founded by the Mewar scion Maharana Udai Singh II, in 1559 CE. After the emergence of

The City of Lakes-Udaipur

artillery warfare in the 16th century, he decided to move his capital to a more secure place as he had realised the importance of this aspect during his exile in Kumbhalgarh. One day, while hunting in the foothills of the Aravalli range, he met a hermit named Goswami Premgiriji. The hermit blessed him and asked him to build a palace on the shoreline of a lake which is now called Lake Pichola. He assured him his new capital would remain well protected. Prophetic words! Maharana Udai Singh II decided to shift his entire kingdom to Udaipur. Being a mountainous region and unsuitable for heavily armoured Mughal horses, Udaipur remained safe from Mughal influences in spite of pressure from surrounding areas. Udaipur remained as the capital city till 1818 when it became a Princely state of British India and thereafter the province became a part of Rajasthan when India gained its independence in 1947," Hema ended her historical account as she turned to purchase entry tickets to The City Palace on our behalf.

Udaipur City Palace

The City Palace of Udaipur looked imposing and truly aristocratic. When viewed from Lake Pichola, its magnificence takes one breath away.

Maharana Uday Singh had initiated the construction of the palace. Thereafter, succeeding Maharanas added several palaces and structures to the complex, retaining the uniformity of design. The entry to the palace is from the Hathi Pol, The Elephant Gate. The Bari Pol or the big gate brings one to Tripolia, the triple gate. As we entered the palace to have a quick tour, we were impressed to see arched balconies, cupolas and towers surmount the palace to give a wonderful view of the lake.

Hema kept up her nonstop commentary about the palace.

"The City Palace of Udaipur is a superb anthology of art works that trace the fascinating stories of the rise of Udaipur city, the riveting saga of the Mewar dynasty and the life of the bravest warrior of Mewar, Maharana Pratap and his beloved horse Chetak. It is ironic that the palace's core structure was completed for Maharana Pratap to come and rule, but his vow to defeat the Mughals made him spend his life in jungles, and thus, he never visited this place."

"Oh!" we exclaimed.

We soon came upon a unique exhibit of Maharana Pratap with his horse Chetak. Hema enquired whether Jean Pierre and Gaidik had heard of Chetak. They shook their heads.

"Chetak has gone down in the annals of history for his unmatched love and devotion to his master, Maharana Pratap. He has been eulogised in several couplets and poems and will always be identified with Maharana Pratap. He was a lion on the battlefield. He had all the makings of a great war horse-strength, stamina, swiftness, saddle-trained and sure-footed. In the battle of Haldighati, Chetak sustained a deep cut on his leg when Rana Pratap attacked the elephant of Man Singh. Sensing his master's life to be in danger, the injured Chetak galloped away from the battlefield and covered a safe distance. But he finally collapsed after jumping over a twenty two feet stream and died a valiant death." She pointed at the exhibit, "What you see here is a portrayal of a spectacular anecdote of how Maharana Pratap put the mask of an elephant's trunk on the face of Chetak to confuse the rival Mughal Army's elephants."

Maharana Pratap with Chetak

"Fascinating," said Gaidik. I felt proud of being an Indian with a glorious historical background which was replete with incidents of valour, courage, sacrifice, dedication, faith, and love.

It was past noon when we stepped out of the City Palace. Our itinerary consisted of visits to Saheliyon-Ki-Bari, Jagmandir, Lake Palace and last but not least was Bagore Ki Haveli.

"Tell us something about Bagore Ki Haveli, Hema," Kalpana ma'am said as we headed towards it. We were supposed to stay there for dinner after an evening of music and dance.

"Bagore Ki Haveli is a 700-year-old historical monument with a checkered history. Until about 30 years ago, it had been in disrepair. It is now a very interesting museum where you can get lost in gorgeous artwork and a captivating ambience. We are going to stay on till the evening to enjoy one of the best nights of our entire trip with foot-tapping Rajasthani music and dance." Hema's remark thrilled all of us.

"That sounds like we are going to have one of the best times of our life!" Rajeev exclaimed. We agreed enthusiastically.

A cultural treat awaited us that evening. We were mesmerised to see the graceful movements of the three Teratali folk dancers who belonged to the Kamar tribe. Each performer had an ornamental pot on her head and a sword clenched between the teeth.

Similar to Teratali folk dance and even more exhilarating was the Bhavai dance. Traditionally the dance is performed by female performers belonging to the Jat, Bhil, Raigar, Meena, Kumhar and Kalbelia communities. Our guests from France gasped in wonder to see the young nimble-footed dancers pirouetting with numerous metal pitchers on their heads with fire lit up to nine pitchers. What actually took our breath away was their balancing act which they did standing on either a glass tumbler or on the edge of a sword in tandem with music.

"Why so many pitchers!" exclaimed Gaidik, awestruck.

"It is assumed that this dance evolved from the exceptional balancing skills of the females who used to be forced to carry a number of pots of water on their head over a long distance in the desert," said Hema.

"What an ingenious way to make drudgery into a creative performing art!" admired Jean Pierre.

The next dance we saw was Ghoomar, which we were told was performed traditionally by the Bhil community. Much to our delight, we all were made to get up and join the group of performers who moved very gracefully in a circle. I felt gawky and stiff while Meera and Priyamvada blended in with equal grace. So did Kalpana ma'am and Gaidik. It was hilarious to watch the boys emulate

Bhavai Dance

the feminine moves with a silly grin plastered on their face. What fun we had just before dinner, we were completely enraptured by the performance of the highly energetic Kalbelia dance. We were intrigued to know that in 2010, the Kalbelia folk songs and dances of Rajasthan were declared a part of its Intangible Heritage List by UNESCO. The show hosts told us that this dance form took its name from the tribe of its origin, Kalbelia. These tribes were traditionally snake catchers and traded snake venom. Hence the dance movements and costumes bear a resemblance to serpents.

The sheer pace of music and the intense energy of the performers put us in a complete trance-like state.

"Hey!" I exclaimed, "In Assam we have something on similar lines! It is called Deodhoni dance which is a Shamanic folk dance of Assam. It is associated with the worship of the snake goddess Manasa or Maroi as called by a few people. Originating from the Bodo Kachri tribe, Deodhoni is usually a group performance but may

Kalbelia Dance

also be performed solo. It is usually accompanied by songs sung by an Ojha, an Assamese traditional chorus leader. Dancers are known to get into a trance-like inspired state, as they move to the beats of the Ciphung (flute) and the Kham (drum). At one stage of the dance, performers even take a sword and a shield performing a virile war dance, honoring various gods and goddesses, like Shiva, Lakshmi, etc."

We were struck by the similarities in the dance styles of Rajasthan and Assam- in spite of the fact that these two States were more than two thousand kilometres away from each other.

On this note, we proceeded for dinner. The place was teeming with visitors from all over the world. While enjoying yet another round of traditional Rajasthani cuisine, our table was visited by the Director of the performing arts group, Mr Shankar Dev. A thin, tall gentleman with streaks of silver grey hair tied in a ponytail and a smart salt and pepper French beard, he walked up to our table as he was curious to see a group of students along with some foreign guests. After an initial round of introductions, we invited him to join us for dinner. He agreed graciously. And were we glad to have him! The conversation with Mr Shankar Dev left us enlightened on the little known subject of Intangible Heritage.

"Cultural heritage may be tangible heritage like physical artefacts or intangible heritage like oral traditions, performing arts, etc. It is an expression of the way communities have developed their ways of living and have thereafter passed it from one generation to another through customs, practices, places, objects, values and so forth," said Shankar Da as he was popularly known.

The crowd had started thinning out. We were soon joined by the members of Shankar Da's troupe. On Jean Pierre's request, Shankar Da agreed to tell us about a few intangible heritage domains of Rajasthan and Assam.

Chapter 20

WEALTH OF INTANGIBLE HERITAGE

The traditional craftsmanship of the unique art form from the village of Molela, in Rajasthan, is part of the intangible heritage of this State. Known by the name of Votive Terracotta, the plaques are made

Molela Terracotta

from clay mixed with rice husk and donkey dung in required proportions. The plaque is sun-dried and baked in an indigenous kiln before it is painted with mineral colours and eventually coated with a local made lacquer, called 'jala'. This is a skill and an art which needs to be preserved."

Shankar Da paused to have a sip of water.

"You heard about the Kalbelia dance being part of the list of intangible heritage, even the practice of turban tying in Rajasthan is a part of our cultural heritage."

We recalled vividly the joy on the faces of Jean Pierre, Bhuvan Sir, and the boys as they tried out the various turbans in Mehrangarh fort.

Shankar Da continued, "Turban tying is a complex mechanism. Each community has its own unique style of wearing this outfit. The earliest evidence of the element is available from a 2nd century BC statue of the Kushana period, depicting a woman wearing a turban. So during that time, the turban was probably tied without any gender distinction, unlike the later years where turban tying was relegated as an exclusive male domain. The modern turban is around 300 years old, and is worn now by men only. British ethnographers of the colonial period have recorded the phenomenon vividly. Today, the turban is a symbol of pride and identity. Also, it has several practical uses. The turban can be used as a pillow, a mattress, or a rope to draw water from wells. Rajasthan is a desert state, so the ubiquitous turban also keeps the head temperature cool by allowing the wearer to perspire profusely in the heat which in turn cools the body temperature."

"Oh wow! We never thought of that!" said Rajeev and Meera simultaneously.

"And I always wondered why the men wear such big turbans in the scorching heat of summer. Now I know," smiled Gaidik.

Another jewel in the list of intangible heritage crafts is the tradition of Phad paintings. Phad is an approximately thirty feet long and five feet broad painted scroll which depicts stories of local deities and legendary heroes. These are rendered musically by the local priests called Bhopa.

Rajasthani Turban

"It is enriching to know about these crafts and talents. What I don't understand is why they have been enrolled in the UNESCO list of intangible heritage domains? I mean, what is the purpose of identifying certain traditions and customs and skills as intangible heritage?" I asked, puzzled.

"Superb question, young lady!" exclaimed Shankar Da. I blushed, embarrassed at being addressed as a young lady.

"Intangible culture is not just about our cultural heritage to boast of, rather it is a wealth of skills and knowledge that is transmitted from generation to generation. This knowledge not only has social and economic value but what is more important is the transmission of skills for minority groups and mainstream groups within a state. If not preserved, these will soon become extinct. These dying arts need to be identified and preserved for progeny. Much of our old knowledge and skills is lost due to non-awareness. Now, we should not let this happen. One has to strive to conserve the roots and originality of a society to maintain the rich character of our nation."

"So much to understand and appreciate!" Priyamvada exclaimed.

Shankar Da ordered a round of special masala chai for all of us, as he started speaking about the intangible heritage domains of Assam.

"Have you heard of the Assamese satras?" asked Shankar Da.

"Yes, I think we heard about it while talking of Majuli islands..." Gaidik said hesitatingly and looked at me to confirm what she had said. I nodded and she continued in a more confident voice, "I recall these are institutional centers associated with spiritualism as well as the arts and crafts of Assam."

Shankar Da nodded his head in agreement and continued speaking, "Sattriya tradition is a composite body of numerous artistic expressions combining music, dance, theatre, and other allied arts which has a great impact on both spiritual and social life of Assam. Steeped in intense spiritual fervour and deep educational value, the Sattriya tradition has a great influence on the Assamese culture. What sets it apart is the distinct style of music and dance which has major influences of pan-India and Indo-Mongoloid traditions. It is completely different from North and South Indian music and dance."

"In fact, two more domains of the intangible heritage wealth of Assam may be attributed to Mahapurusha Sankradeva, the Father of Assamese culture. One is an instrument called Khol which is egg-shaped like a mridangam and originally was made of clay. Nowadays, Khols are made of wood. And the next is the Ankiya

Satra Theatre in Majuli

Nat, the traditional Assamese theatre. Ankiya Nat has managed to survive till the present day more or less in its original form."

Shankar Da paused to take a sip of tea and continued, "In Assam, there is a festival or rather a festive occasion called Pachoti which is celebrated by the people of Assam. This too, figures in the UNESCO list of intangible heritage. The word Pachoti comes from Sanskrit word 'Pancha' which means five. It is celebrated on the fifth day of the birth of a baby, especially a baby boy since the tradition relates to the birth of Lord Krishna. The main part of the ceremony is deciding the name of the baby. In some parts of Assam, Pachoti is celebrated in different places on the fifth or eleventh day, and sometimes even after a month of a baby's birth."

Seeing his audience getting restless, Shankar Da quickly changed his tone and said, "Now, let me tell you my favourite Assamese intangible heritage. It is unique in its ownself. It is called The Jun Beel Mela. This Mela or fair is a centuries-old traditional fair which seems to be a virtual wonder in its own right. The most striking feature of this historic fair is that it has been keeping alive the age-old barter system as a means to procure goods. This Jun Beel Mela is organised every year in mid-January, near the highway town of Jagiroad in the Marigaon District of Assam. The three day annual event is being organized under the traditional king of the Tiwa tribes called 'Gobha Deoraja' that once ruled the area. What is most interesting to see is the ease with which goods are exchanged and traded without using cash. One could never imagine a barter system could exist so successfully in this day and age. The fair is also considered a very important instance of maintaining cordial relations between the people residing in hills and the plains as well as among the tribes and non-tribes."

"I could have never envisaged an active barter system in this day and age," Jean Pierre remarked softly.

It was unique, indeed!

Shankar Da looked at us and said, "You are fortunate to understand what intangible heritage is at such a young age. With the awareness you children have gathered, I have high hopes for the conservation of this heritage for the next generation. We are on the verge of losing some of the best folklores, folk tales, dances, music, oral traditions and social practises at the altar of a digital world today. With more and more things becoming digitilised and commercialised, these rich traditions which are the core strength behind India's immense diversity, are under a constant threat of becoming extinct. So do whatever you can to keep up the traditional arts alive." He ended on a serious note.

"Speaking of performing and fine arts, Shankar Da, would you please tell us about Rang Ghar?" I asked the ebullient gentleman.

"Ah! The Rang Ghar!" exclaimed Shankar Da with joy. A sudden shift took place in his demeanour and he was back to his old, cheerful self. "It is not only one of the most fascinating structures of Assam but is also the oldest amphitheater in Asia which was constructed in the 18th century. During

Rang Ghar (Assam)

Rongali Bihu, the greatest festival of Assam, Rang Ghar used to be the royal sports pavilion, from which the Ahom kings and nobles witnessed games in the Rupahi Pathar- the field where these games were played."

"What kind of games?" asked Gaidik.

"In olden days people enjoyed watching elephant, buffalo, bull and hawk fights, wrestling, etc." Shankar Da paused once again and looked around at the group. By now, we could identify that this look meant that he was about to say something dramatic.

"Do you know, according to me, what is the most striking feature about this building?" Shankar Da asked with glinting eyes. Greeted by silence, he looked at us with a triumphant look, glad to see the callow audience.

"The Ahoms used special thin, baked bricks for construction sans cement. Instead of cement they used a paste of rice and eggs as mortar for construction, a pulse called Maati Maah and a fish named Borali Mach in Assamese." To Shankar Da's sheer joy, every member of the group had incredulous looks on

Talatal Ghar

their faces. We were not too surprised as something similar had been used in Ahom Raja's palace too. Nevertheless it was very interesting. We decided that once we reached home we would research the binding qualities of these unusual items which were used instead of cement.

"Rather, I would say, cement has become the substitute of these natural ingredients," Meera murmured.

Shankar Da continued, "If you go to Assam, you must visit one of the grandest examples of Tai Ahom architecture called Talatal Ghar.

It is located quite close to Rang Ghar. It is also called The Rangpur Palace. This place was initially built as an army base. Interestingly, Rang Ghar supposedly houses two secret tunnels which are located three floors below ground level. These were used as exit routes during the Ahom wars. Hence the name Talatal Ghar. The Rangpur palace is actually a seven-storied structure but only the ground floor to second floor is now open to visitors."

"We have seen numerous forts, palaces and secret tunnels in Rajasthan. It is good to know about Assam too," Meera said with a smile.

It was quite late in the evening. We thanked Shankar Da and his troupe and finally decided to call it a day.

The next day would herald the last day of our whirlwind physical tour of Rajasthan coupled with a verbal -virtual tour of Assam.

Time flies is an adage I had heard. This was the first time I experienced it. It was with mixed feelings of joy and sadness that we retired for the night.

Chapter 21

ADIEU!

It was once again cold and foggy as we embarked upon our journey back to Jaipur. We were informed by the driver that the journey would be approximately an eight hour one. We could not see anything out of our windows due to the dense fog. A few of us dozed off and it was Gaidik's voice which made everybody wake up fully.

"I have been thinking about the position of women in Rajasthan and Assam. I wonder, are their problems the same?"

Kalpana ma'am replied thoughtfully, "Interesting question, Gaidik. I don't think we have ever thought on these lines. Nevertheless, as far as I can surmise, the entire region of the North Eastern part of our country, which includes Assam, is free from some of the social evils like dowry, Sati, female foeticide and infanticide, unlike many parts of North India, especially Rajasthan."

"And why is it so?" asked Gaidik. Even we were surprised to hear this. Kalpana ma'am seemed to be in deep thought and spoke hesitatingly, "I think it is because of the prevalence of tribal and indigenous culture in and around Assam," she continued her thoughtful observations, "I am sure there are other forms of gender discrimination that exist there as is evident from various gender gap studies which have taken place several times over the years."

"What is a gender gap? And why do we always speak of empowering women?" Rajeev asked petulantly ,his eyebrows knitted in consternation. Everybody's face broke into a big smile. We could see that the topic bothered Rajeev. Gauransh, on the other hand, looked cool as a cucumber.

"Rajeev, gender gap is the difference between women and men as reflected in social, political, intellectual, cultural, or economic attainments or attitudes. The World Economic Forum in the year 2005 introduced The Global Gender Gap Index or GGGI to capture the magnitude and scope of gender based inequalities. And to answer the second part of your question, I will tell you very briefly why there is a need to talk about women empowerment. Time and again, several studies have revealed the subordinate status of women in relation to men in almost every facet of life. Since the past few decades the world has witnessed a steady increase in awareness of the need to empower women to eradicate the gender gap and thus achieve gender equality." Kalpana madam's words enlightened all of us.

"Oh alright," Rajeev heaved a sigh of relief. "I thought all talks of women empowerment happen to make women stronger and more powerful than men!"

We laughed aloud at his honest confession. Gauransh did not find anything funny in what Rajeev had spoken. Probably he may have shared Rajeev's apprehensions! However, his next question was an interesting one which elicited an equally interesting response from Kalpana ma'am.

"What exactly does gender equality mean?"

"Gender equality is understood as that stage of human development wherein the rights, responsibilities and opportunities of individuals are not to be determined by the fact of being born as male or female. It is a stage when both men and women realize their full potential and become partners in every sphere of their life. I would like to quote Swami Vivekananda here who said it is impossible to think about the welfare of the world unless the condition of women is improved. It is impossible for a bird to fly on only one wing."

"That is such an empowering thought in itself!" exclaimed Gaidik.

We nodded our heads enthusiastically in agreement.

"Apart from the government schemes, which I am sure, must be catering to empowerment of women, do citizens also reach out to help each other?" asked Jean Pierre.

"Yes!" Meera and I said simultaneously and burst out laughing thereafter. "Alright Debina, let's hear you first," said Kalpana ma'am with a smile.

"I don't know much, but would like to share whatever little I know," I began modestly. "My mother had volunteered in Assam Centre for Rural Development (ACRD) which is a registered non-government organisation that came into existence in 1995. Late Dr Lily Mazinder Baruah, a renowned social activist of the North Eastern region and youngest daughter of Bharat Ratna Lokapriya Gopinath Bordoloi, first Chief Minister of Assam, played a key role in giving birth to ACRD. I think it was around 2010 that a project was undertaken which covered five hundred women belonging to the tribal and other backward communities for promotion of livelihood through pig rearing. Under the project, ACRD imparted training on pig rearing in a scientific and systematic way to the women identified in the Block. Awareness programmes were organised, which addressed issues on mother and child health, food and nutrition, laws related to women's issues, environment, etc. Self Help Groups were formed by women from 36 villages of the Block. They were given two piglets each, along with a pig shed. They were also given training on financial management, skill building, management and marketability of the products, health and hygiene, proper feeding and veterinary care, artificial insemination etc. As far as I know, the project is now over, but I remember my mother telling me that it helped the beneficiaries enormously." I paused to catch a breath.

"Pig farming!" Gauransh exclaimed in surprise.

"Wow! One could have never thought of this in a place like Rajasthan!" Priyamvada said.

It was Meera's turn to speak now, "A unique saga of empowering rural men and women in Rajasthan is the

Barefoot College which was started by Shri Bunker Roy. What started as a program that focussed on water and irrigation changed to a program on empowerment and sustainability. Influenced by the Gandhian philosophy of each village being self-reliant, the policy of Barefoot College is to take students, primarily women from the poorest of villages and teach them skills such as installing, building and repairing solar lamps and water pumps without requiring them to read or write. In extreme cases, there are students without verbal fluency in the language of their teachers."

"This is fabulous!" cried Jean Pierre, "It just goes to show that a skill does not always require an academic degree to be learnt! With proper training, it can be picked up by anyone who is interested," we agreed.

Priyamvada spoke up next, "I would like to speak about the phenomenal work being done by Princess Diya Kumari Foundation for women empowerment. This Foundation started in the year 2013, by the Founder of our school, Princess Diya Kumari, who is an entrepreneur, a philanthropist, an art connoisseur and a Member of Parliament too," she looked around at all members of the group with a look of pride. We echoed her sentiments.

"Don't forget, she has been the ambassador for the Beti Bachao Beti Padhao campaign of the government," added Rajeev quickly and translated the name of the campaign in English for our guests.

"A true champion for women's cause, I must say," said Gaidik admiringly. "Yes," we chorused happily. Priyamvada continued, "The Foundation is a non-government organisation which is a philanthropic social outreach initiative. The program areas are skill building, health and hygiene, education and capacity building in agricultural practices. PDKF, as the Foundation is popularly called, has worked extensively towards uplifting the lives of underprivileged women and girls in Rajasthan where literacy rates are low and women cannot progress given the economic and socio-cultural barriers.

Princess Diya Kumari with PDKF ladies

It provides skill building to create sustainable livelihoods. Apart from this, PDKF is doing commendable work in the field of girl child education. The Shiksha Diya Project was started by PDKF in a few schools wherein the organization has offered scholarship and material support to girls while creating awareness on topics like menstrual hygiene as well as providing digital literacy programs. They have also been acclaimed by the UN Women Committee of Canada for empowering women by providing them financial literacy workshops."

We were thrilled by the applause from our guests.

Meera took over now, "You have seen our land is rich in both tangible and intangible heritage. The Foundation has been instrumental in promoting this heritage by training women in craft, embroidery, stitching and soft toy making."

Priyamvada ended the topic on an interesting and unique note, "PDKF recently struck a partnership with a famous online marketplace called Airbnb that connects people who want to rent out their homes with people who are looking for accommodations in that area. The idea was not only to display the hospitality of Rajasthan but also to give rural women an idea of micro-entrepreneurship as they open their houses to welcome Airbnb guests."

"That is truly a very unique way of empowering rural women to become entrepreneurs!" Gaidik exclaimed. "Please do take me to the PDKF outlet. I would love to buy small mementos for family and friends from there. It will give me an opportunity to tell them about the PDKF story."

We agreed happily.

The journey passed off in a blur. We were surprised when the vehicle entered the school premises. Much to our dismay we realised that it was over!

We bid tearful goodbyes and returned to our respective homes.

Jean Pierre and Gaidik left Jaipur the next day. Kalpana ma'am and Bhuvan Misra sir went to drop them at the airport. They had promised to get in touch with us.

We heard from them a month later. Our Principal, Dr Sadhna Singh called us to her office to congratulate all of us for representing the school so well. We jumped with joy when she showed us the formal letter of partnership between Saint Beatrice School and The Palace School.

Mission fulfilled.

Another surprise awaited us. Dr Sadhna Singh gave us the mementoes that Gaidik and Jean Pierre had sent across. We were stunned to get copies of a beautiful painting made by them for all of us. The painting was titled, 'The Camel With A Japi- an intermingling of two vibrant cultures.' It had a few puppets, a camel wearing the traditional Assamese hat called Japi and the most interesting feature was the Eiffel Tower!

I shall always cherish their gift and the memories of the whirlwind tour we had. It gave us the opportunity to understand and appreciate the

The Memento

rich legacy we have inherited from our ancestors. We have understood the importance of conserving and preserving our culture, customs, and rich biodiversity. We have learnt to appreciate our unity in diversity.

I promise to uphold the true spirit of Ek Bharat Shreshtha Bharat.

Adieu.

Adieu

GLOSSARY

Alpana 1	Alpana or alpona refers to colourful motifs, sacred art or painting done with hands and paint which is mainly a paste of rice and flour on auspicious occasions in Bengal.
Ambilineal Descent 2	(noun) Tracing an individual's descent either through the father or mother as chosen by the individual.
Amlokhi 3	In Sanskrit, the word Amalaki means "the sustainer", Amalaki has long been used as a natural remedy by practitioners of Ayurveda, an alternative medicine system that has its roots in ancient India. Amalaki (Êmblika officinalis) is a fruit with a bitter taste that's not usually eaten on its own, but instead prepared as part of a meal or condensed into a supplement.
Ashwamedha yajana 4	The Ashvamedha (Sanskrit: अस्वमेध aśvamedha) is a horse sacrifice ritual followed by the Śrauta tradition of Vedic religion. It was used by ancient Indian kings to prove their imperial sovereignty: a horse accompanied by the king's warriors would be released to wander for a period of one year. In the territory traversed by the horse, any rival could dispute the king's authority by challenging the warriors accompanying it. After one year, if no enemy had managed to kill or capture the horse, the animal would be guided back to the king's capital. It would be then sacrificed, and the king would be declared as an undisputed sovereign.
Astrolabe 5	An instrument used by early astronomers to measure the altitude of stars and planets and also as a navigational aid. It consists of a graduated circular disc with a movable sighting device.
Aura 6	The distinct quality that seems to surround or come from somebody or something.

Azimuth 7	The direction of a celestial object from the observer, expressed as the angular distance from the north or south point of the horizon to the point at which a vertical circle passing through the object intersects the horizon.
Baati 8	Baati is a hard, unleavened bread cooked in most of areas of Rajasthan, It is prized for its long shelf life and high nutritional content, and, in desert areas, for the minimal quantity of water required for its preparation. Baati is commonly eaten with dal, hence also referred to as dal baati.
Baoris 9	A Stepwell, as baori is one of the Hindi and Urdu terms for a stepwell
Beris 10	Small community wells for drinking water
Besan Sattu 11	Sattu is prepared by dry roasting grains or gram (besan), most often barley or bengal gram. Sattu sharbat is a healthy summer drink made with roasted gram flour.
Bhaonas 12	A mythology-based theatrical performance.
Carbon footprints 13	A measurement of the amount of carbon dioxide produced by the activities of a person, company, organization, etc.
Declination 14	Is the angular distance of North & South from the celestial equator.
Dumb waiter 15	A small lift for carrying things, especially food and crockery, between the floors of a building or a movable table, typically with revolving shelves, used in a dining room.
Ephemerides 16	A table giving the future positions of a planet, comet, or satellite. 2. an annual publication giving the positions of the sun, moon, and planets during the course of a year, information concerning eclipses, astronomical constants, etc.
Ethnographers 17	A person who studies and describes the culture of a particular society or group.
Fact geek 18	A person who has excessive enthusiasm for and some expertise about a specialized subject or activity.
Gandharva rites 19	A Gandharva marriage (Sanskrit: गन्धर्व विवाह) (known as love marriage) is one of the eight classical types of Hindu marriage. This ancient marriage tradition from the Indian subcontinent was based on mutual attraction between two people, with no rituals, witnesses or family participation.
Gender Stereotypes 20	Personal beliefs about gender differences in traits and behaviour, largely attributable to socialization.
Haat 21	A haat bazaar, most often called simply haat or hat, is an open-air market that serves as a trading venue for local people in rural areas and some towns
Hardpan 22	A hardened impervious layer, typically of clay, occurring in or below the soil and impairing drainage and plant growth.
Indus Valley	Indus civilization, also called Indus Valley civilization or Harappan civilization,

Civilization 23	the earliest known urban culture of the Indian subcontinent.
IUCN Red List 24	The International Union for Conservation of Nature (IUCN) Red List of Threatened Species (also known as the IUCN Red List or Red Data Book), founded in 1964, is the world's most comprehensive inventory of the global conservation status of biological species.
IVRI 25	Established in 1889, the Indian Veterinary Research Institute (IVRI) is one of the premier research institutions dedicated to livestock research and development of the region.
Jamun 26	Blackberry
Kair sangri 27	Capparis decidua is commonly known as kair. The berries can be eaten and mixed with sangri (beans from the tree Prosopis cineraria) to form a vegetable dish called "Kair sangri" in Rajasthan, India, which is a delicacy to many.
Krantivritta 28	Revolutionary circle or the path
Linear 30	Arranged in or extending along a straight or nearly straight line.
Logging tool 31	Logging tools developed over the years measure the electrical, acoustic, radioactive, electromagnetic, and other properties of the rocks and their contained fluids.
Mehenga 32	A special kind of plate, made from bamboo for offering the food.
Musak 33	Ganesha's vehicle—the mouse
Oxbow lakes 34	A curved lake formed from a horseshoe bend in a river where the main stream has cut across the narrow end and no longer flows around the loop of the bend.
Puranas 36	The word Purana literally means "ancient, old", and it is a vast genre of Indian literature about a wide range of topics, particularly legends and other traditional lore. The Puranas are known for the intricate layers of symbolism depicted within their stories.
Rangoli 37	A traditional Indian art form using coloured sand or powder to decorate a floor, courtyard, or other flat surface.
Rasivalaya or Zodiac Circle 38	Rasivalaya are instruments for measuring the celestial latitude and longitude of the celestial bodies. There are twelve instruments which represent the twelve signs of the zodiac, one for each measurement to be done when the corresponding sign of the zodiac transits the meridian.
Seri culture 39	Sericulture, or silk farming, is the cultivation of silkworms to produce silk.
Shilpa Sastra 4 0	Literally means the Science of Shilpa (arts and crafts). It is an ancient umbrella term for numerous Hindu texts that describe arts, crafts, and their design rules, principles and standards. In the context of Hindu temple architecture and sculpture, Shilpa Shastras were manuals for sculpture and Hindu

iconography, prescribing among other things, the proportions of a sculptured figure, composition, principles, meaning, as well as rules of architecture.

Step wells 41	Originating from the Indian subcontinent, Stepwells are wells or ponds in which the water is reached by descending a set of steps to the water level. They may be multi-storied with a bullock turning a water wheel to raise the well water to the first or second floor.
Swastikas 42	In Sanskrit, the word swastika is a combination of 'su' (meaning 'good') and 'asti' (meaning 'to exist') Popularly, this gets translated as 'all is well.' The swastika is thus understood to be a symbol of auspiciousness and good fortune, and is regularly donned on Hindu homes, businesses, printed materials, cars, temples, and ashrams.
Unnatamsa 43	Elevation/altitude
Urns 44	A tall, rounded vase with a stem and base, especially one used for storing the ashes of a cremated person.
Xokota 45	It's severely bitter type of preparation. It's prepared with dry jute leaf, matimah (urad bean) and khar.

WEBLIOGRAPHY

1) "The Indian Mona Lisa". Medium, 2021, https://medium.com/the-collector/the-indian-mona-lisa 59b3be2108c5. [Accessed 14 November 2020].

2) Informatics, I. (n.d.). Login: Register: I-RAS: Dharmashastra National Law University Library, Jabalpur. Retrieved December 31, 2020, from https://shodhganga-inflibnet-ac in.dnlulib.remotlog.com/ [Accessed 14 November 2020].

3) India's Largest Review Platform. (n.d.). Retrieved December 31, 2020, from https://www.mouthshut.com/ [Accessed 14 November 2020].

4) Asiguwahaticircle.gov.in. 2020. Archaeological Survey Of India (ASI), Guwahati Circle, Assam. [online] Available at: <http://asiguwahaticircle.gov.in/Bishnudol%20Gaurisagar.html> [Accessed 15 November 2020].

5) Thomas Cook India Travel Blog. 2020. City Palace Jaipur - Everything You Need To Know About | Thomas Cook Blog. [online] Available at: <https://blog.thomascook.in/city-palace- jaipur-rich-culture heritage/> [Accessed 15 November 2020].

6) India, T. and India, T., 2020. Explore The City Palace Museum During Your Visit To Jaipur. [online] Tour My India. Available at: <https://www.tourmyindia.com/blog/the-city-palace- museum-jaipur/> [Accessed 15 November 2020].

7) Pareek, A., 2020. City Palace The Home Of Jaipur Royals | History || Architecture || Rajasthan|| India |. [online] http://amerjaipur.in/Amer-monuments description.php?mid=12&name=City%20 Palace%20Jaipur. Available at: <http://amerjaipur.in/Amer monuments description.php?mid=12&name=City%20Palace%20 Jaipur> [Accessed 15 November 2020].

8) Pareek, A., 2020. Govind Dev Ji Temple History, Visiting Hours, Tourist Attractions Jaipur Rajasthan, India. [online] http://amerjaipur.in/Amer-monuments description.php?mid=6&name=Govind%20Dev%20JI%20Temple. Available at: <http://amerjaipur.in/Amer-monuments description.php?mid=6&name=Govind%20Dev%20JI%20 Temple> [Accessed 16 November 2020]. 9) 2020. [online] Available at: <https://www.jaipur.org.uk/temples/govind-devji-temple.htmlCh –> [Accessed 16 November 2020].

10) 2020. [online] Available at: <https://www.en.m.wikipedia.org> [Accessed 16 November 2020].

11) Jantar Mantar. 2020. Home | Jantar Mantar. [online] Available at: <https://www.jantarmantar.org/> [Accessed 16 November 2020].

12) Hawa-mahal.com. 2020. About Hawa Mahal | Hawa Mahal. [online] Available at: <https://www.hawa-mahal.com/information-about-hawa-mahal/> [Accessed 17 November 2020].

13) https://www.nativeplanet.com. 2020. 7 Interesting Facts About Hawa Mahal In Jaipur. [online] Available at: <https://www.google.com/amp/s/www.nativeplanet.com/amphtml/travel guide/interesting-facts-about-hawa-mahal-001739.html> [Accessed 18 November 2020].

14) Lonely Planet. 2020. Hawa Mahal | Jaipur, India Attractions. [online] Available at: <https://www.lonelyplanet.com/india/rajasthan/jaipur/attractions/hawa-mahal/a/poi sig/449393/356451> [Accessed 18 November 2020].

15) Hippie In Heels. 2020. 39 Places To Visit In Jaipur For The Trendy Traveler - Hippie In Heels. [online] Available at: <https://hippie-inheels.com/places-to-visit-in-jaipur> [Accessed 20 November 2020].

16) Livehistoryindia.com. 2020. Live History India : Stories That Make India. [online] Available at: <https://www.livehistoryindia.com/> [Accessed 20 November 2020].

17) "Government Of Assam Department of Cultural Affairs." Home | Department of Cultural Affairs | Government Of Assam, India, culturalaffairs.assam.gov.in/. [Accessed 20 November 2020].

18) Welcome to Rajasthan - Official Website of Department of Tourism, Government of Rajasthan, www.tourism.rajasthan.gov.in/. [Accessed 20 November 2020]

19) "Palace on Wheels." Palace on Wheels : A Royal Journey through Luxury Train, www.thepalaceonwheels.org/. [Accessed 20 November 2020].

20) "India Tourism: The Incredible Travel Guide to Visiting India: Tour My India." Tour, www.tourmyindia.com/. [Accessed 20 November 2020].

21) Deejayrocks2. "Nahargarh Stepwell 02.Jpg." Nahargarh_stepwell_02.Jpg, 12 Sept. 2019, commons.wikimedia.org/wiki/File:Nahargarh_stepwell_02.jpg. [Accessed 25 November 2020].

22) "Nahargarh Water Walk." Heritage Water Walks, 16 Sept. 2019, heritagewaterwalks.com/nahargarh-water-walk/. [Accessed 25 November 2020].

23) "Oh My Rajasthan! Culture: Places Tourism: Festival." Oh My Rajasthan! Culture | Places Tourism | Festival, www.ohmyrajasthan.com/. [Accessed 25 November 2020].

24) "Main Page." Wikipedia, Wikimedia Foundation, 10 Nov. 2020, www.en.m.wikipedia.org/. [Accessed 25 November 2020].

25) "User:Onef9day." User:Onef9day - Wikimedia Commons, commons.wikimedia.org/wiki/User:Onef9day. [Accessed 28 November 2020].

26) "Manuscript Painting of Assam: In Conversation with Rupeswar Nath." Sahapedia, www.sahapedia.org/manuscript-painting-of-assam-conversation-rupeswar-nath. [Accessed 29 November 2020].

27) "Manuscript Painting of Assam: Historical and Contemporary Perspectives." Sahapedia, www.

sahapedia.org/manuscript-painting-of-assam-historical-and-contemporary-perspectives. [Accessed 2 December 2020].

28) "Kaziranga National Park & Tiger Reserve Assam, India." Kaziranganationalpark, 16 Jan. 2020, www.kaziranga-national-park.com/. [Accessed 2 December 2020].

29) "SoftSchools.com Provides Free Math Worksheets, Free Math Games, Grammar Quizzes, Free Phonics Worksheets, and Games. Worksheets and Games Are Organized by Grades and Topics. These Printable Math and Phonics Worksheets Are Auto Generated." Free Math Worksheets, Free Phonics Worksheets, Math Games and Online Activities and Quizzes, www.softschools.com/. [Accessed 2 December 2020].

30) "Ranthambore National Park." Ranthambore National Park | Ranthambhore Tiger Reserve - Sawai Madhopur, Rajasthan, www.ranthamborenationalpark.in/. [Accessed 5 December 2020].
31) Centre, U. (n.d.). Kaziranga National Park. Retrieved December 31, 2020, from https://whc.unesco.org/en/list/337/ [Accessed 7 December 2020].

32) Personalized Wildlife Safaris & Tiger Tours. (n.d.). Retrieved December 31, 2020, from https://www.tigerwalah.com/ [Accessed 7 December 2020].

33) Centre, U. (n.d.). Manas Wildlife Sanctuary. Retrieved December 31, 2020, from https://whc.unesco.org/en/list/338/ [Accessed 7 December 2020].

34) "Tecomella." Wikipedia, Wikimedia Foundation, 7 Mar. 2020, es.m.wikipedia.org/wiki/Tecomella. [Accessed 7 December 2020].

35) "File:The magnificent Ganges River Dolphin.jpg." Wikimedia Commons, the free media repository. 2 Sep 2020, 11:57 UTC. 31 Dec 2020, 08:35 <https://commons.wikimedia.org/w/index.php?title=File:The_magnificent_Ganges_River_ Dolphin.jp g&oldid=446976553>. [Accessed 17 December 2020].

36) "File:Capped langur in manas.jpg." Wikimedia Commons, the free media repository. 20 Dec 2020, 13:47 UTC. 31 Dec 2020, 08:37 <https://commons.wikimedia.org/w/index.php?title=File:Capped_langur_in_manas.jpg&oldi d=52000 8440>. [Accessed 17 December 2020].

37) "File:Gaur-Bos gaurus.jpg." Wikimedia Commons, the free media repository. 24 Oct 2020, 05:57 UTC. 31 Dec 2020, 08:39 <https://commons.wikimedia.org/w/index.php?title=File:Gaur Bos_ gaurus jpg&oldid=499001391>.[Accessed 17 December 2020].

38) Manas National Park, Manas, National Park of Manas, Manas Wildlife Sanctuary in Assam, Manas Wildlife Reserve, Wild Life in Manas Sanctuary, Manas Wild Life, Manas Tiger Reserve, National Park in Assam, Manas National Park Tour, manasnationalpark.net/. [Accessed 8 December 2020].

39) Centre, UNESCO World Heritage. UNESCO World Heritage Centre, whc.unesco.org/. [Accessed 8 December 2020].

40) K, Rashmi. "Your Guide to Nature and Wildlife Travel." Wildlifezones.com, wildlifezones.com/. [Accessed 8 December 2020].

41) "Why Should I Care about Endangered Species?" Mongabay Environmental News, 12 Aug. 2017, news.mongabay.com/2016/01/why-should-i-care-about-endangered-species/. [Accessed 11 December 2020].

42) RajRAS. "Mines & Minerals of Rajasthan: RajRAS - Rajasthan RAS." RajRAS, 1 June 2020, www.rajras.in/rajasthan-mines-minerals/. [Accessed 12 December 2020].

43) Rahman, Jiyaur. "Mineral Resources of Assam: Sillimanite, Clay, Sand,Iron Ore, Copper, Gypsum and Other Minerals of Assam." Www.abhimanuias.com, 2020, abhipedia.abhimanu.com/Article/State/NDQ5MgEEQQVVEEQQVV/Mineral-resources-of- Assam---Sillimanite--Clay--Sand--Iron-Ore--Copper--Gypsum---other-minerals-of-Assam- Assam-State. [Accessed 25 December 2020].

44) "History." Mehrangarh Museum Trust, www.mehrangarh.org/mehrangarh-2/history/. [Accessed 25 December 2020].

45) Books, ACC Art, and Accpublishinggroup. "JODHPUR LANCERS." Issuu, issuu.com/accpublishinggroup/docs/jodhpur_lancers_blad. [Accessed 01 January 2021].

46) Rao Jodha Desert Rock Park, www.raojodhapark.com/. [Accessed 01 January 2021].

47) Editor|, Resham SengarResham Sengar|Times Travel. "The Story of Mehrangarh Fort and Its Curse." Times of India Travel, 13 Feb. 2019, timesofindia.indiatimes.com/travel/destinations/the story-of-mehrangarh-fort-and-its- curse/as67977077.cms. [Accessed 01 January 2021].

48) Welcome to Kamrup District, Assam, India. History, Geography, Administration, Project Sualkuchi, Madan Kamdev,e-Suvidha, kamrup.nic.in/. [Accessed 01 January 2021].

49) "ASSAM GOVERNMENT." Assam.gov.in, assam.gov.in/. [Accessed 01 January 2021].

50) Samvaad, Dhanush. "Ministry of Tribal Affairs, Government of India." Ministry of Tribal Affairs - Government of India, tribal.nic.in/. [Accessed 02 January 2021].

51) "RAJ RAS: RajRAS - Rajasthan RAS." RajRAS, 16 Jan. 2021, www.rajras.in/. [Accessed 02 January 2021].

52) "Home." Radically Ever After, 8 Aug. 2019, radicallyeverafter.com/. [Accessed 02 January 2021].

53) CatchNews.com, Catch Hindi, www.catchnews.com/. [Accessed 03 January 2021].

54) Rawat, Rajendra. Rainwater Harvesting - Solution to Water Crisis - Technology and Systems, www.rainwaterharvesting.org/. [Accessed 03 January 2021].

55) Kumar, Mayank. "Rajasthan's Architectural Marvels of Water Conservation." The Wire: The Wire News India, Latest News,News from India, Politics, External Affairs, Science, Economics, Gender and Culture, The Wire, 1 July 2017, m.thewire.in/article/society/rajasthan-architectural-marvels water-conservation. [Accessed 03 January 2021].

56) Shah, Aditi. "How Oil Was Found in India." Live History India : Stories That Make India, Live History India, 26 June 2019, www.livehistoryindia.com/snapshort- histories/2019/06/26/how-oil-was-found in-india.. [Accessed 04 January 2021].

57) "5 Ways Falling Oil Prices Affect India - Meaningful Minutes." Kotak Securities®, kotaksecurities.com/ksweb/Meaningful-Minutes/5-ways-falling-oil-prices-affect-India. [Accessed 04 January 2021].

58) Singh, Karunjit. "Explained: Why India Is Producing Less and Less Oil." The Indian Express, 30 June 2020, indianexpress.com/article/explained/explained-why-indias-crude-oil-production-as been-falling-6479345/. [Accessed 04 January 2021].

59) "ENVIS Centre: Assam Status of Environment and Related Issues." Status of Environment Related Issues: Assam ENVIS Centre, Ministry of Environment and Forests, Govt. of India, asmenvis.nic.in/database/energy_858.aspx. [Accessed 04 January 2021].

60) RajRAS. "Power Resources of Rajasthan: RajRAS - Rajasthan RAS." RajRAS, 2 Mar. 2020, www.rajras.in/power-resources-of-rajasthan/. [Accessed 04 January 2021].

61) Upsy. "LEARNING FROM THE WORLD." UNCONVENTIONAL AND VIVID, 11 Oct. 2020, unconventionalandvivid.com/. [Accessed 05 January 2021].

62) "Home." Stories by Soumya, 22 Jan. 2021, www.storiesbysoumya.com/. [Accessed 06 January 2021].

63) Expert, NE Travel. "THE TIWA TRIBE." NE Tribe, www.ne.cab/tribe/the-tiwa-tribe. [Accessed 06 January 2021].

64) Raksha. "Australian and Indian Blogger!" SOLOPASSPORT, 27 Jan. 2021, solopassport.com/. [Accessed 10 January 2021].

65) RatnakarSadasyula, and RatnakarSadasyula Follow. "EKLINGJI'S KINGDOM." Wattpad, www.wattpad.com/346591460-land-of-the-ranas-eklingji%27s-kingdom. [Accessed 14 January 2021].

66) NationalViews, Team. "Why the Rulers of Mewar Used the Title Rana and Not Raja or Maharaja?" National Views, 5 July 2020, nationalviews.com/rulers-of-mewar-title-rana- meaning-facts-. [Accessed 16 January 2021].

67) "India Today Education - Breaking News, Results, Exams, Education Updates and Notifications." News, www.indiatoday.in/education-today. [Accessed 20 January 2021].

68) Rajvanshi, Nehal, et al. Live History India : Stories That Make India, www.livehistoryindia.com/. [Accessed 21 January 2021].

69) "Stories of Animals, Nature, and Culture." National Geographic, www.nationalgeographic.com/. [Accessed 25 January 2021].

70) Udaipur-Rajasthan. "Home." Udaipur, www.udaipur.rajasthan.gov.in/. [Accessed 28 January 2021]. 71) "Tertali." Wikipedia, Wikimedia Foundation, 11 Aug. 2019, en.wikipedia.org/wiki/Tertali.

72) "Bhavai Dance." Wikipedia, Wikimedia Foundation, 26 Jan. 2021, en.wikipedia.org/wiki/Bhavai_dance.

73) "Ghoomar." Wikipedia, Wikimedia Foundation, 24 Jan. 2021, en.wikipedia.org/wiki/Ghoomar#:~:text=Ghoomar%20is%20a%20traditional%20folk,wear%2 0flowin g%20dresses%20 called%20ghaghara.

74) "Kalbelia." Wikipedia, Wikimedia Foundation, 22 Jan. 2021, en.wikipedia.org/wiki/Kalbelia.

75) "Dances of Assam." Dances Of Assam - Folk Dances of Assam, Traditional Dances of Assam, www.bharatonline.com/assam/dance/index.html. [Accessed 30 January 2021].

76) "Category:Rituals." Category:Rituals - Wikimedia Commons, commons.wikimedia.org/wiki/Category:Rituals. [Accessed 30 January 2021].

77) "Home." Stories by Soumya, 26 Mar. 2021, www.storiesbysoumya.com/. [Accessed 30 January 2021].

78) Expert, NE Travel. "THE TIWA TRIBE." NE Tribe, 27 Apr. 2020, www.ne.cab/tribe/the-tiwa-tribe. [Accessed 30 January 2021].

79) Team, LHI. "Shree Eklingji & the Maharanas: In the Service of God." Live History India: Stories That Make India, Live History India, 21 Nov. 2018, www.livehistoryindia.com/snapshort histories/2018/11/21/shri-eklingji-the-maharanas-in- the-service-of-god. [Accessed 1 February 2021].

80) Kochhar, Aashish, et al. Live History India : Stories That Make India, www.livehistoryindia.com/.

81) National Geographic, www.nationalgeographic.com/. [Accessed 2 February 2021].

82) Deodhoni Dance Ritual-1.jpg. "Deodhoni Dance Ritual-1.Jpg." Wikimedia Commons, commons.wikimedia.org/wiki/File:Deodhoni_Dance_Ritual-1.jpg. [Accessed 5 February 2021].

83) Https://Commons.wikimedia.org/Wiki/File:Molela_(Mus%C3%A9e_du_ Quai_Branly)_(4489837962). Jpg. [Accessed 7 February 2021].

84) "Polo." Wikipedia, Wikimedia Foundation, 1 Apr. 2021, en.wikipedia.org/wiki/Polo. [Accessed 7 February 2021].

85) "Polo Handicap." Wikipedia, Wikimedia Foundation, 2 Apr. 2021, en.wikipedia.org/wiki/Polo_handicap#:~:text=A%20polo%20handicap%20is%20a,from%20mi nus%2 D2%20to%2010. [Accessed 7 February 2021].

86) "What Are the Benefits of Wind Power?: ACCIONA: Business as Unusual." ACCIONA, www.acciona.com/renewable-energy/wind energy/#:~:text=Wind%20energy%20is%20a%20source,gasses%20that%20cause%20global% 20w arming.&text=For%20these%20reasons%2C%20producing%20electricity,use%20contributes% 20to %20sustainable%20development. .[Accessed 7 February 2021].

87) Ritchie, Hannah. "What Are the Safest and Cleanest Sources of Energy?" Our World in Data, ourworldindata.org/safest-sources-of-energy. [Accessed 7 February 2021].

88) "Great_Hornbill." WIKIMEDIA COMMONS, upload.wikimedia.org/wikipedia/commons/d/d6/Great_Hornbill_%28Buceros_bicornis%29_-_Flickr_-_Lip_Kee_%281%29.jpg. [Accessed 8 February 2021].

89) Gaur-Bos Gaurus.jpg. commons.wikimedia.org/wiki/File:Gaur-Bos_gaurus.jpg. [Accessed 8 February 2021].

90) Capped_langur_in_manas.Jpg. commons.wikimedia.org/wiki/File:Capped_langur_in_manas.jpg. [Accessed 8 February 2021].

91) File:MUKHA SILPA, Majuli, Assam.jpg - Wikimedia Commons. commons.wikimedia.org/wiki/File:MUKHA_SILPA,_Majuli,_Assam.jpg. [Accessed 8 February 2021].

92) Phad_painting_of_rajasthan_india.Jpg. ko.wikipedia.org/wiki/%ED%8C%8C%EC%9D%BC:Phad_painting_of_rajasthan_india.jpg.

93) Molela_(Mus%C3%A9e_du_Quai_Branly)_(4489837962).Jpg. commons.wikimedia.org/wiki/File:Molela_(Mus%C3%A9e_du_Quai_Branly)_(4489837962).j pg. [Accessed 8 February 2021].

94) Deodhoni_Dance_Ritual-1.Jpg. commons.wikimedia.org/wiki/File:Deodhoni_Dance_Ritual-1.jpg. [Accessed 8 February 2021].

95) "Old Manuscripts of Assam." Sahapedia, www.sahapedia.org/old-manuscripts-of assam#lg=1&slide=12. [Accessed 8 February 2021].

96) Google Image Result for Https://Upload.wikimedia.org/Wikipedia/Commons/4/4b/Bhavai_is_a_genre_of_folk_danc e_popular _in_Rajasthan._The_male_or_female_performers_balance_a_number_of_earthen_pots_while_ dan cing.Jpg, images.app.goo.gl/XpWAse5VWxVtWRW8A. [Accessed 11 February 2021].

97) Thumb/4/47/Jaisalmer_forteresse.Jpg/1280px-Jaisalmer_forteresse.Jpg. [Accessed 11 February 2021].

98) Google Image Result for Https://Upload.wikimedia.org/Wikipedia/Commons/4/4f/Royal_Bengal_Tiger.Jpg, images.app.goo.gl/c8bikocRTufhgVLK8. [Accessed 11 February 2021].

99) Science., Wagner Free Institute of. "Transactions of the Wagner Free Institute of Science of Philadelphia." V.3:Pt.1-3 (1890-1895) - Transactions of the Wagner Free Institute of Science of Philadelphia., Wagner Free Institute of Science of Philadelphia, 1 Jan. 1890, www.biodiversitylibrary.org/item/98240. [Accessed 11 February 2021].

100) "File:Golden Oriole from Dresser's Birds of Europe.jpg." Wikimedia Commons, commons.wikimedia.org/w/index.php?curid=83737691. [Accessed 11 February 2021].

101) Metmuseum.org, www.metmuseum.org/art/collection/search/37788. [Accessed 11 February 2021].

102) Google Image Result for Https://Upload.wikimedia.org/Wikipedia/Commons/Thumb/1/1e/Walls_of_Shish_Mahal% 2C_Lahore _Fort.Jpg/1200px-Walls_of_Shish_Mahal%2C_Lahore_Fort.Jpg, images.app.goo.gl/hyGg5CEtT1wG3GbC7. [Accessed 11 February 2021].

103) Limited, Alamy. "Stock Photo - Krishna Battles the Armies of the Demon Naraka: Page from a Bhagavata Purana Manuscript, Ca. 1540." Alamy, www.alamy.com/krishna-battles-the- armies-of the-demon-naraka-page-from-a-bhagavata-purana-manuscript-ca-1540-image343009462.html?pv=1&stamp=2&imageid=E2AE70AF-1269-4800-B10D